LONDON YEARS

MICK McCARTHY

Kildanore Press,Blanchardstown, Dublin 15. 1990

LONDON YEARS
Copyright © Mick McCarthy 1990
Cover design : Fran Dempsey
Photography : John Kennedy, The Green Studio
Limited, Dublin.
Hand Tinting : Willie Finnie
Editing : Margaret Kelleher

Printed by Colour Books Limited Dublin,
and the Guernsey Press.

Typeset by Kildanore Press and
Typelink Limited, Dublin
Film Separations by Irish Photo Limited, Dublin

Dedication

*I dedicate this book to all those, both young
and old, who are living rough through no fault
of their own...*

Publishers Note

In May 1990 Kildanore Press published Mick McCarthy's first book - *Early Days*. *London Years* is the continuation of that story. For readers who haven't read *Early Days* the prologue consists of part of the last chapter from the first book.....

A review of *Early Days* in the Irish Times:

"Mick McCarthy has been in his time a publican, trade unionist, father-figure of the Irish ballad-singing world and general all-round large pinch of the salt of the earth, so it's no surprise that his first book of reminiscences, Early Days, is as gentle, funny and perceptive as the man himself.

Kerry long ago is the location - in and around the town of Listowel, to be more precise - and we see it through the eyes of a small boy, first in stirring Black and Tan times, with raids and uncles on the run, and then through the bitterness of the Civil War.

After that there are first jobs, and a first romance that ends in tragedy with a drowning. Then our hero is off to pastures new, travelling to Limerick under a train seat to avoid paying, and stowing away on a tramp steamer delivering pigs to Liverpool. Pre war England with its huge unemployment and poverty must have seemed a savage and lonely place for a penniless, solitary Irish boy. Yet such was his openness, resilience and attractiveness that he seems to have made friends everywhere he went.

Volume two, London Years,is promised. If it's as beguiling and easy to read as this one we're in for another treat."

Fergus Linehan

Prologue

"Got great news for you," Mrs Diver announced as I got in from work one evening. It was her half-day and I could smell the dinner cooking.

"Irish Stew?" I said.

"Irish Stew my granny. Mr Stein was at the Club for lunch today, he wants you to call and see him in the morning,he's going to make you a suit. What do you think of that?"

"I don't believe it," I said.

"Well, you can believe it. You must be the luckiest guy ever to come out of Kerry. He wants another photo for the window of his shop. I'll tell you something," she said laughing. "I wish he'd take a few photographs of Arthur."

"Where is Eileen?" I asked.

"Oh! she left a note to say she's meeting somebody in Hyde Park at eight o'clock."

All the good news and Mrs Diver's invitation to 'just taste that Irish Stew' suddenly were of no importance. If only I knew who it was that Eileen had gone to meet.

After helping with the washing up,I decided to take a walk to Speakers' Corner. Every step of the way my mind grew more numb with jealousy,despair and disbelief.

Once again the place was crowded. At least a dozen speakers were vigorously proclaiming everything from Euthanasia to Life Everlasting. It was then I saw Eileen and her friend. The man was *tall,dressed immaculately in a blue suit and trilby. My worst fears confirmed,I stood gazing long after they disappeared through the gates.*

All around me speakers and hecklers were going through their standard routine. Fascists,Latter Day Christians, Conservatives,Free Thinkers. Great excitement as one and all worked up the passions of their respective audience. Their vehemence about the state of affairs in this world or prospects for the next,to me right now meant nothing - just nothing. My world had collapsed before my very eyes.

Scarcely aware of a steady drizzle I joined the stragglers and staggered unsteadily on to the Edgware Road. My mind in a whirl,any plan for present or future beyond consideration. The drizzle by now turning to heavy persistent rain,did much to ease the burning in my head. One thing was clear,I would never again return to 217 Westbourne Grove. Sometime I must write to Mrs Diver and Arthur to thank them for all their kindness.

The new suit from Mr Stein? That and my job,gone but not forgotten. Must make a clean break. How could I face Mrs Diver at the Club?

Vaguely conscious of the heavy traffic rushing to and fro - heavy rain always sure to bring the taxis out in droves...

Jesus, how could this happen? Could it be,she was unaware of how madly I loved her?

The sound of Irish music and loud conversation interrupted my thoughts. The doors of the Black Lion were open wide, a steady cloud of smoke drifting outwards to be caught in the rain and soft breeze,suddenly to disappear. If I closed my eyes I would have no trouble believing I was in the busiest pub in Listowel during a Horse Fair. Irish accents of every hue and shade. Not a woman in sight.

Trying in vain to reach the counter I brushed against a tall man standing in company. Suddenly, he turned around and put his hand on my shoulder. "Jesus Christ man," he said. "You're wringin'."

His tone of surprise made his mates laugh. "Could feel the water soak right through to my arse," he went on to more laughter. "Hould on there," he ordered, "I'll get you a drink." Before I could utter a protest he was halfways to the counter.

"Don't arg' the toss with Big John," one of his mates advised. "His heart is as big as his fist."

In less than a minute, Big John was back with a tray laden with pints and glasses of whiskey. "Get that down you," he said, handing me a large whiskey. "Might, just might stop you getting pneumonia."

I started to thank him for his kindness but no words came. My mind was in turmoil. So many things had happened since my arrival in London: Eileen; Mrs Diver; Arthur, and his accident; Deirdre the nurse, and that awful nightmare in jail.

I suddenly became aware that it had been the constant company and charm of Eileen which had occupied me so much that I had failed to pursue my affair with Deirdre......

"Take another whiskey." Big John's voice cut across my thoughts.

"No thanks," I heard myself reply. "I'd best be going." I stood up, mumbled something like a goodbye and made my way to the door.

"Time now gentlemen please," the barman yelled.

Still raining. Unsure of what to do next, my visit to the pub and the drink doing little to clear my mind. No hope of lodgings in any house in my state, and at such an hour. Yet it was my only hope. I could be in Lisson Street within a few minutes. One more night in the 'biggest bedroom in the world', neither here not there.

Across the street on a hoarding huge letters lit by a street lamp: JOIN THE ARMY AND SEE THE WORLD - THE MILL HILL REGIMENT WELCOMES YOU.

Jesus, here we go again. What a pity it's not the French Foreign Legion. My mother. I know she would understand, if I should ever get a chance to explain.

Arriving in Lisson Street I knocked at the huge door. Dripping rainwater I sat on the wet step, feeling sick and exhausted.

"Are you stone deaf? I'm not standing here all night," the gruff voice said. "I take it you have your tenpence?"

Slowly, I got to my feet and shuffled into the hallway. The heavy door closed with a sound like thunder behind me, shutting out the cold night.....

Chapter One

"THE third passageway on your right", the night porter said as he opened the doorway to the biggest bedroom in the world. The mad orchestra of coughing and snoring was far worse than I remembered from my first visit. This time, my bed was far away from the solitary electric light and, once again, I was more than glad to discard my soaking wet clothes.

Even were I in the most comfortable bed in London, sleep would be out of the question. Staring at the dark ceiling, all I could see was the laughing face of Eileen as she gaily waltzed through the gates of Hyde Park with her immaculately dressed Guardsman. How quickly life can change from optimism and joy to absolute despair. All night long, the heavy rain pelted down on the huge flat roof like a thousand mad drummers harmonising with the crazy orchestra. Once or twice, the rhythm was broken by a shrill screech as somebody wakened from a ghastly nightmare.

The sound of the orderly shouting "wakey wakey" was a welcome change of tune. Hastily donning my wet clothes, I scrambled down the steps onto a bright sunlit street. My clothes would soon dry out in Hyde Park and hopefully I would get an hour or two of much needed sleep.

It was to be short-lived. Tired as I was, a vicious jab in the backside made me jump, certain I was being bitten by a dog. A man in a black uniform and a peaked cap was standing over me. He held a walking stick with what looked like a dagger at its end.

"Thought a prod in the awrse would wake you up," he said. "Can you not read?"

"Read what?" I said.

"There's a notice at every entrance,Paddy," he snarled, "Vagrants,beggars,soliciting or sleeping out in the Park,strictly forbidden. What makes you so sleepy this time of the day?"

"A long story."

"Don't get smart wiv me,Paddy," he said. "You could be in the nick for a week or two if I decided to charge you...."

I felt relieved he said 'if'.

He walked around the tree and came back with a french letter dangling from the stick. "This yours?" he asked. My sudden outburst of laughter must have tickled his sense of humour.

"Thought not. She'd want to be off her chump. Sit on a bench or keep walking," he barked,as he trotted away with his stick and sack.

Not far from Marble Arch on the Edgware Road, I came to a huge building site. On impulse I went in. "You'll find the ganger in his office. Up the street and in the far gate," a workman advised.

"Come in,come in," the voice barked. Opening the door,I almost tumbled back down the three steps. Facing me was the huge figure of 'Big John', my unexpected benefactor at the Black Lion the night before. A smile creased his handsome face as he pushed the newspaper to one side. "Well 'pon my soul," he chirped,"if it's not my old segotia. Thought you'd never dry out again."

"Not so sure that I have," I replied,"but that's another long story. Any chance of a job?"

Sizing up my dishevelled uniform,a remnant from my job at the Illustrated Paper Exchange, Big John broke into a hearty laugh. "Matter of fact your luck is in," he said. "Our tea-boy is leaving the firm after thirty years . Inherited his brother's farm in Roscommon, a mighty man until the years caught up with him. Ould Paddy will show you the ropes for a day or two,then you're on your own." Rising from his seat, his head almost touching the ceiling; "let's go and meet Paddy," he said.

In the big shed at the back of the site, Paddy turned from the work in hand and greeted us cheerfully.Turning off the water tap,he placed a shining mug on a huge bench beside a hundred more. "Ready for action," he said,nodding his head towards three blazing fires at the back of the shed. Over each a five gallon steel boiler emitted steam from its bouncing lid. "No bother to you Paddy," said Big John.

"A Bobby's job," Paddy gaily remarked,both men sensing my feeling of shock and uncertainty. "OR-GAN-IZATION - that's the key," Paddy continued. "The milk is delivered. Keep your sugar and tea well stocked up. Slip out for the men's cigarettes and tobacco after lunch. Write down what money they give you after each man's name and Bob's your uncle. Rake your fires out and reset them. Fill your boilers,wash up the mugs and you have the rest of the day to yourself."

"You're a lucky man you turned up here today," Big John said. "The cushiest job in the firm." Far from convinced, I emphasised I would have a go.

"I'll look for some digs," I said, "and start in the morning." To my utter astonishment Big John put his hand in his pocket and handed me a ten bob note. "A sub," he said.

"You're a trusting man," I replied.

"Never backed a loser yet. Welcome to the firm," he quipped as he headed out the door to start a tour of inspection.

I was lucky indeed that Paddy could stay for two days to give me the benefit of his experience,and OR-GAN-IZATION. Without any doubt, this had to be the busiest job in London. I was glad when Saturday came. Being a half day, no need to light the fires. Just general cleaning up and preparations for the week ahead. "By the way," Big John said, putting his head in the shed door, "there's a very good dance in the Carlton,Shepherds Bush, Saturday and Sunday night. Might see you there?"

"In this gear?" I said.

"Nobody will even notice how you're dressed, the place will be that full."

"Great," I said. "I'll be seeing you."

To my surprise Big John was on the door at the dance hall. Two more men, almost as big as himself, stood beside him. He beckoned me past the cashier's window. "Glad you made it. We won't charge you tonight. Loads of girls in there, so have a good time."

The hall was packed and there seemed to be two girls for every man. However that situation would change rapidly as soon as the pubs closed.

When the barndance was announced, I plucked up courage and asked a girl up. She seemed to be on her own. She was very friendly and asked me if I had seen George.

"George?" I said, "I don't think I know him." Laughing she said, "I thought everyone knew George. He's my brother. My name is Colette. Here he comes,do excuse me I'll be back to you later."

The band was still playing,but the talking and laughing had suddenly died down. George Logan was standing inside the door surrounded by six or seven men,as big as the ones on the door. Colette was dragging him by the arm indicating the far side of the hall where a few vacant seats were left. Slowly the hall got back to normal. I decided to leave my dancing partner with George,at least for the time being.

"Are we in for trouble?" I said to a man standing beside me.

"No way, no way," he whispered back. "There's never a problem in an Irish dance or pub when George is around."

George and his friends were now seated with Colette sitting on his knee. A bottle of whiskey was being passed from one to the other.

"It's a crying shame," the man beside me went on, "George was heavyweight champion of the Irish Guards at eighteen. Nothing or nobody could stand with him in the ring. He put Jack Doyle away in the first round of the army semi-finals. Just couldn't be tamed. No time for authority of any kind. Took up all-in wrestling. Steve Casey, heavyweight champion of the world thought he had a world beater in him, but alas that bottle won every time."

The band started up an old time waltz. Colette came running across the floor.

"Are you right?" she said, "I told you I'd be back. George is okay now."

As we took the floor, abruptly the band stopped playing, and the shrill sound of a black maria could be heard outside the door. Colette pulled me after her to the hallway.

"It's not moving," she whispered. "This could mean trouble."

"That's Bill Ryan talking to George," she said. "He's George's best friend. Tommy Murphy and himself run the dances here. Let's go and find out what's happening."

George Logan and his friends were now standing in a circle around Bill Ryan. George walked slowly to the centre of the dance floor. There was dead silence in the hall, while the sound from the sirens outside became ever more piercing.

"They've come for a showdown," George announced. "All to do with the Harrow Road row on Saint Patrick's night, you all know what happened then."

"What happened, Colette?" I whispered.

"A policeman was killed," she replied. "And they'd love to pin it on George."

About thirty men slowly moved towards the centre of the floor.Bill Ryan spoke for the first time. "There's enough table legs and chair legs for everyone. They're in the dressing room at the back."

Surely, I thought, any time now I'm going to wake up. This has to be a dream.

"Open all the doors wide," I heard George tell Bill Ryan. "This is it."

Ryan waved up to the band and immediately they started playing a set of reels.

"Let's go to the front hall," Colette said. "George will be the main target and I'm really worried."

Within minutes the scene outside was indescribable. Three black marias were lined up outside the door, their windscreens smashed to smithereens. A fourth black maria was lying on it's side, sirens still screeching. Policemen and civilians lay in grotesque shapes all over the road. George was at the far side , his back to the wall, his face covered in blood. Bill Ryan and another man came from somewhere and two of the three policemen attacking George were floored. Bill staggered towards the door and yelled; "run in and tell the band to stop the music. Listen, tell Duffy to announce that we want more men out here. We must finish this off before reinforcements arrive."

Big John staggered in through the door. Tearing off his shirt,he ripped it in two and held it to a gaping wound on the side of his head. In a matter of seconds he was back in the middle of the road, his chair leg flaying in all directions.

A gang of men went streaming out through the door, all armed with cudgels. Two of them returned immediately with George, who was obviously in a state of collapse. Colette and three or four girls helped him through to the back of the hall. Somebody handed him a glass of whiskey.

"We'll get him out to Jerry Ryan's lorry in the laneway," Colette said. "If they get him to the barracks they'll just kill him this time. Get hold of Jerry Ryan," she told me. "Tell him we must get away now before reinforcements arrive."

After much shouting somebody found Jerry Ryan. He came staggering through the door, his coat and shirt in tatters. He was rushed to the back of the hall and the glass of whiskey once again appeared like magic.

"The laneway is clear, Jerry," Colette said. "Larry Murphy and his mate are in a bad way too, so let's get moving. Give me a hand with George."

"Sure thing," I replied, happy to be going anywhere.

"We're going to Murphy's place," Jerry told Colette. "There's an Irish doctor living next door, he's a sound man. Keep everybody lying down on the lorry, at least till we get away."

Tommy Murphy and his wife were out of bed in a flash, and soon a huge pot of water was boiling on the gas. Everything was done without fuss and with very little talk. Mrs Murphy made a big pot of tea.

The doctor arrived, a handsome looking man of about forty. "Nellie," he said, "before we start work, give me a drop of the hard stuff."

"I'll have a drop of the crater too, Nell," George said, sitting up on the couch and clicking glasses with the doctor. "Your health," he toasted, as they both started laughing. Everyone else joined in.

C OLETTE shook me awake. I was lying on the floor and could have stayed there for a week. "It's six-thirty," she said. "We'll get seven o'clock Mass at Marble Arch. I have to be in work at eight in St Mary's Hospital."

"I didn't know you were a nurse," I said.

"I'm not. But I will be some day."

We jumped off the bus at Marble Arch. Colette caught me by the hand and within seconds we had arrived at what looked like an ordinary hall door,except that it had a crucifix above the knocker. Colette put her finger to her lips as we entered. The church was about thirty feet long and just wide enough to seat two abreast from the door to the altar. Six nuns took up the front seats and members of the public the rest. Colette and I were lucky to get the last two inside the door. When communion was served, Colette stepped past me and moved sideways towards the altar. I lowered my head between my hands and had to bite my lip to avoid laughing.

"You know," she said as we walked towards St Mary's Hospital, "that's the world's smallest church. At least that's what they say and nobody claims otherwise. The Convent is at the back and the little church used to be the tradesman's entrance. The nuns got tired of courting couples and going out to Mass, so they killed two birds with the one stone."

"Did you ever try getting George along?" I asked. She laughed. "Do you know something, George Logan would do anything, I mean just *anything* for me, but no way would he go to Mass. Our dad was excommunicated during the troubles. He was a great I.R.A. man. Not one of our family went to Mass afterwards except me. You see, my aunt was a nun and very kind, so I wouldn't distress her for the world.

"I finish work at four o'clock," she continued, "would you like to meet me?"

"I sure would.That is if you don't mind this admiral's outfit."

"I think it's great," she said. "A lot better than the uniforms we have to wear."

"Do you think the dance hall will be open tonight?" I asked. "No way," she said, as she climbed the steps to the front door of the hospital. "That's a goner. Don't worry, there will soon be another." She threw me a kiss and disappeared through the door.

I headed for the Serpentine and went to sleep on a bench. It must have been the hunger and thirst that woke me.I enquired the time from a passer-by who told me it was three-thirty.Time to meet Colette.

Reaching Kensington Gardens we found a quiet spot under a huge oak tree and with my arms around her she dropped off to sleep within minutes. The courting couples passing by seemed to be highly amused. I wasn't sure whether it was my uniform or Colette stretched out fast sleep, or both, which caused their mirth. The remarks were choice. I could do nothing but laugh. How could they know how little I cared about their taunts. How proud and happy I felt lying beside this charming light-hearted girl. My only concern was that she wouldn't turn up for our next date.

"Had a letter from my mother today," she said, as we met the following Thursday evening. "Dad is not well, George is badly needed at home. My mother doesn't realise it's useless talking to him. Why he stays over here when the police have such a down on him beats me. Up to the time he left home he loved farming, and especially horses."

"Do you think I will meet with his approval?" I asked.

"Don't talk so daft," she retorted. "My boy friends are my own business."

"Boy friend? Did you say boy friend?" With a sharp dig in the ribs, Colette jumped up as the tram came to a halt. We linked arms up the street and were still linking as Colette rang Murphy's doorbell. As the door opened we reeled around laughing; George was standing in the doorway.

Mrs Murphy was busy preparing dinner. "A lovely stew," she said cheerfully.

"Smells great," Colette said, as she went to the kitchen leaving me alone with George.

"A Kerryman?" he said. "Well, well... ever met the Casey's?" Without waiting for my reply.... "we beat Cork on Sunday," he shouted to Colette.

"That's good news anyway."

It was hard to believe this huge man relaxing in the couch had been right at the centre of so much turbulence so short a time before.

"Big John tells me he's taken you on as tea boy," Tommy Murphy said as we sat down to dinner. "Do you like the buildings?"

"Very much," I replied. "I worked on the buildings at home."

"Oh! fancy that. I had a word with your boss on Saturday night, I'm looking for a couple of lads keen to learn bricklaying. Are you interested?"

"Am I interested?" I said, "I can hardly believe my ears."

"It's like this. You'll have to do two evenings a week out here in my garden learning the bonds, how to build corners etc. Then you would have to go to the Tech. next winter."

"Tommy," said I, "this is the best news I have ever heard."

"Right then. Give Big John notice tomorrow and tell him you won't leave till he has another teaboy broken in."

MY first day with Tommy Murphy was a strange one indeed. The whole day I was put on my own with a pile of bricks in the middle of a concrete floor. I had to put up a corner five or six courses and pull it down again. I learned Flemish bond and old English bond, how to spread mortar, how to use a hammer and chisel, and to cut closures. If I can remember all these things I'll be a bricklayer in no time at all, I thought.

"Can't put you on a wall," Tommy said, "until I'm sure you won't be holding up the gang. There's no profit in that. See you in the morning. Make sure you shine that trowel before you go home. A good tradesman keeps his tools shining."

I fixed my nights at Murphy's to coincide with Colette's visits. Most nights there was a music session. Murphy's was a regular meeting house for traditional musicians. Usually we had to run for the last bus to Paddington, where I had managed to get digs near the hospital.

"I'm getting my holidays next week," Colette told me. "I'm going home for two weeks. I'm praying I can get George to come with me. Things are getting very serious at home and Dad is not improving."

After spending the whole weekend with George, without success, Colette was very depressed as I saw her off at Paddington Station. "I'll write every day," she said. "Be good and no flirting while I'm away."

Sadly I made my way to the pub just outside the station. I had barely started on my pint when George came through the swing doors with three of his friends. "I missed her," he said. "That bastard of a bus."

"She knew something like that happened," I lied. "She told me to tell you she will write as soon as she gets home."

One of his friends bought four whiskeys and a

pint for me. The whiskeys disappeared in a flash.

"Right," George said, "we'll be cutting along. We have a bit of business to sort out. Mind yourself, and tell the Murphy's I'll be over to see them one of these nights."

I stayed a long time over my pint and returned to the digs feeling very sad.

JIMMY Palmer, my new mate, was a Dublin man, the first Dublin man I had ever met. Two of his brothers also worked on the job, also bricklayers.

"Keep a cool head," he said, as we got on the scaffold. "I had a few jars last night and I don't feel too good. Think you can manage that corner on your own?"

"I'll give it a good try."

"Keep it right anyway," he said, "or we're in big trouble with Tomser Murphy."

Jimmy took the other corner and, sick head or not, he had it scaffold high in an hour. He rambled over and took a squint at my work. "Good. Get on the line and I'll finish it off." I had been worried at the thought of getting a new mate, but Jimmy was a nice guy.

"Tell me," he said, a couple of days later. "Have you made up your mind to make a career out of this game?"

"Of course," I said, "I love it."

"Well then. We'll have to get you into the Union."

"That would be great," I said. "Do you think they will take me?"

"Well, Chalkey over there is Chairman of the branch, so if he has no objection the job is sound. You've served two years already in Ireland, that's the story, so you'll get a third year card. That should help to see you right. The extra coppers here will help make your rate up anyway."

The joining ceremony was quite impressive and included an oath of allegiance. Afterwards I sat with Jimmy to hear the discussion. A man at the front of the hall stood up demanding that the Union take action against a Communist cell trying to stir up unnecessary trouble on his job, the job in question being a Catholic church. His contention was that their agitation amounted to sabotage. "Don't mind your man," Jimmy said, "he's crazy. He's on about something stupid every week. He has Reds on the brain. They call him the Cardinal and he's as remote from reality as all the rest of the Bishops and Cardinals." On a show of hands, the Cardinal's motion was overwhelmingly defeated. "That's a laugh," Jimmy said, "the same man couldn't stack bricks on a lorry."

COLETTE was expected back at the weekend. Only one letter had arrived and she seemed very depressed, so I was glad to see an envelope on the mantelpiece as I arrived at my digs on Friday night. The very first line confirmed all my fears. "I'm very sorry to tell you I won't be coming back to London for the foreseeable future." I could read no further and put the letter in my pocket.

"Heard bad news then?" Mrs Williams, the

landlady, enquired. "Has something happened?"

"It's my girlfriend. She has to stay at home," I replied. "I was really looking forward to seeing her tomorrow."

"That is terrible for you. Never mind, things will work out alright in the end, you'll see."

I thanked Mrs Williams and went to bed. I lay awake for a long time, too depressed to even think. Colette had been so happy at the nursing and so concerned about George, things must be bad indeed when she felt obliged to stay at home. The stupid uniform never cost her a thought. She would be so pleased with my new suit. The landlady said it made me look real grown up.

Mrs Williams tapped at the door with a cup of tea. "Have your tea and then come on down," she said. "There's a lovely fire and the big boxing match between Ireland and Wales will be on the radio. Maybe we'll have a little bet."

By the time I joined her in the living room, the boxing was over. "Wales has won," Mrs Williams said quite excitedly. If she only knew how little I cared. "Pity we didn't have our bet. There's a good comedy coming on now after the news. I'll give you a glass of wine and we'll try to forget our troubles for a while."

That Christmas, my first away from home, was sad and gloomy. Colette was still in Ireland and had not written. I spent most of Christmas Day in bed, and even the delicious dinner served up by Mrs Williams could not console me.

Chapter Two

WHY didn't I stay in bed, I thought. That wind would skin a cat. Tommy Murphy joined me on the scaffold.

"I'll give you a hand till Jimmy arrives. I have a feeling he won't be in for an hour or two. I know he was meeting George last night." Tommy plucked Jimmy's trowel from the bag. "By the way," he went on, "we have a new dance hall. It's in Cricklewood, maybe you'd come along on Saturday night."

"That's great news Tommy," I said, "it will be nice to see the old crowd again."

"The missus had a letter from Colette. She's very cross you haven't written to her. Her father is very ill, it's a real dilemma for her. Write her a letter tonight and tell her all the news."

"I'll do that," I promised.

"You know," he said, "we didn't have a tune in the house since Colette went home. We miss her an awful lot. Indeed, the missus is talking about going over to visit her when I get my holidays. You'd better start saving up and come over too."

"I had thought very much about doing that Tommy," I said, "but the thought that she might be doing a line with somebody over there makes me undecided."

"Ah! get lost. Don't forget, faint heart never won fair lady."

THE hall in Cricklewood was packed on Saturday night. How the crowd got to know so quickly was a miracle. "Bush telegraph," Tommy explained. "You can't beat it."

Jimmy Palmer,my mate,and his brothers John and Peter arrived.

"Macker," Jimmy said to me, "the clobber looks great."

"He means your suit," Tommy explained.

"These Dublin men are hard to understand. Have a look at his own," he continued mockingly, "I wouldn't wear it going to the bog".

"Come on," Jimmy said, "we'll go and have a few jars, it's a bit early for jiggin' around."

John and Peter Palmer had arranged to meet their girlfriends in the pub. "This is our father," Peter said, introducing Jimmy to Angela and Liz.

"Get stuffed. If I was their father I'd drown the two of them."

Both girls were English, but they enjoyed the crack. "Do you think we'll be safe going in among all those Irish Cailins?" Angela wanted to know.

"Safe," Jimmy said, "they'll be only delighted, you've taken these two nuts out of circulation".

"Come on, girls," Peter said, "let's get out of here before I lose my rag. So long Dad," he teased. "Mind you get home nice and early". Jimmy took a mock punch at Peter, as the four scampered through the door.

"Never mind," Jimmy said, "we'll have one more before facing the music. Only Tommy Murphy is such a good scout, I'd much prefer a game of darts."

Peter was standing inside the door as we arrived.

"Where's everybody?" said Jimmy.

"All dancing," Peter replied. "There's a bastard comes and says 'excuse me' every time I take Angela out. She's very annoyed, but I told her to go along with him. It's the girls' first time at an Irish dance and the last thing we want is trouble."

"There won't be any trouble," Jimmy assured him. "Can I have a dance with her, since you're so decent?"

"Come on Angela," Jimmy said a moment later, "we'll try this quick-step".

The big fellow made a beeline towards Jimmy and Angela before they were half way around the floor,and tapped Jimmy on the shoulder. Jimmy half turned and sent his fist right to the point of the man's jaw. He went down like a sack. John and Peter moved quickly forward, not knowing who might be with the messer, but nobody interfered. Tommy Murphy arrived on the scene and himself and Jimmy lifted the man up and frog-marched him to the door. Tommy shoved the entrance fee into his top pocket. "Get moving," he said, "and don't come back".

"I fancy a pint," Jimmy said.

"You're a mind reader. Just lead the way".

"Any word from Colette?" he asked, as we settled down in the pub.

"It's like this Jimmy," I said, "I'm cheesed off and she's cheesed off, so I can't see any point in swapping sorrows."

"Ah! you take things too serious, gets you nowhere. For my part, I take a girl out, maybe a different one every now and then, but it's casual all along the line."

"You make it sound very easy. Tell me," I said, "have you ever been in love at all, at all?"

He laughed. "Might interest you to know, this kiddo did four months hard labour in the Scrubs because of love."

"You're joking," I said.

"Well I'll tell you, that bastard of a judge wasn't joking. 'I'm sick and tired of Irishmen causing trouble, disturbing the peace and attacking our policemen. Next time you come before me I'll send you packing back to Ireland. Four months with no remission. Hitting and injuring our police will not be tolerated. Let this be a warning to others'."

"That's some mouthful," I said. "May God help George if he goes in front of that judge. What the hell did you do anyway?"

"A long story," Jimmy said. "As I told you it was all for love. Now, are we going back to that dance or not?"

"Let's have another pint," I said, "you must tell me the end of this story!"

"Ah! I never talk about it. Besides, it all happened a long time ago."

"I want to know Jimmy," I said. "Please!"

"*Well*, he said, *it was like this*.... I went out with a girl for over a year in Dublin. Had known her all my life. Maureen and myself, we went everywhere together. She was real good looking, with hair the colour of gold. She loved dancing, and we went twice a week. As you know I have two left feet so I sat most of the dances out. She entered a

competition with a top prize of two hundred quid
for each partner. To make a long story short, she
won the competition with a guy called Larry Doyle.
She kept on telling me how much she disliked this
fellow. He had a swelled head and thought every
girl in Dublin was after him. Anyway, he talked
Maureen into entering for the ballroom
championships over here. The Dublin winners
were eligible. They got nowhere and Maureen was
very disappointed. She wrote to say she was going
to stay with her aunt for a couple of weeks. I went
over to London on the next boat, but her aunt
hadn't even seen her. She just vanished and never
wrote a line to anybody. So that's how I wound up
in John Bull's country. I was just dead lucky to
meet up with Tommy Murphy. Take my tip, if
anybody ever lays a hand on that man, he's sure in
for a sudden death."

"What about the four months in the Scrubs?"

"Well....John and Peter followed me over here a
few years later and spent all their spare time
visiting historic buildings. Walking through the
West End one night they bumped into Maureen.
They decided not to tell me, but Peter blurted it out
when he got drunk. I found her in Bond Street
where Peter said. On the game, sure enough."
Jimmy lit a cigarette. "Like I told you, I don't like
talking about it." A strange look came into his
eyes. There was a long silence.

"Jimmy," I said, "I am sorry. I should have kept
my big inquisitive mouth shut. I'm certain if it was
me I'd have strangled her there and then."

"I might have done just that," he said, "but as soon as we came face to face, she passed out cold in the street. I thought she was dead. Two of her mates were nearby and called a taxi, St. George's Hospital was only minutes away. The girls asked me to wait till she came to. 'She's told us all about you, many many times. It's the story of our lives,' one of the girls said before they took the taxi back to Bond Street. 'Just treat her kindly, she's been through enough already'.

'I want to know none of your business Maureen,' I told her later, as we sat in the pub at Knightsbridge. 'Just tell me where I'll find Doyle.'

'Jimmy,' she said, 'I've made my bed and there's no point raking up the past. I never forgave myself and I never will. The fact is, Doyle and I were all washed up after a month. He wouldn't work and beat me up till I was gone stupid. The people upstairs called the police one night when they heard me screaming. He broke my nose and smashed two of my ribs, but as you see, I survived - well almost.' Her eyes welled up and a trickle of mascara appeared on her cheek. 'Strange isn't it,' she said, in a whisper, 'as much as Doyle hurt me, I never felt as bad as I do now. The past is gone forever and there's no future either. Can I tell you I was a year in Coney Hatch. They said I was mad. I'm attending the doctor every week and I think only the tablets are keeping me going. Up to now I had at least one consolation - that you didn't know and my family didn't know. From now on it just doesn't matter. Call me a taxi, Jimmy, I have to get home. I must get some tablets or I'll pass out. God knows I've caused you enough hardship and heartbreak.' 'Listen, Maureen,' I told her, 'you must do me one favour, that's all I ask. Tell me where I can find Doyle.' 'Jimmy, Jimmy,' she said in a pleading voice, 'Doyle is not worth even talking about. He's real scum. He's now a professional pimp, with two French girls, a Scottish girl and a Greek to manage. I know them. The pimps are a real mafia and stick together. They're really dangerous, they don't stand on each others corns, but if an outsider comes to interfere in any way, they really gang up.' 'Okay, Maureen, please just one last favour. I promise I won't do anything rash.' 'Jimmy, will you really promise, you won't get involved.' 'Cross my heart Maureen.'

'All the pimps drink in the upstairs lounge of the Regent at Piccadilly Circus. They have two bouncers on the door and nobody gets past them. Take the taxi with me, Jimmy, and go straight home. You have your whole life before you and Doyle is not worth a second thought. Come to think of it Jimmy, I'm no better. I've made my own bed and that's that. Before we part, promise me one thing - never breathe a word to any of my family.' 'That you can rely on, Maureen,' I assured her.

"The taxi pulled up just off Baker Street. 'I'll be going on to Willesden,' I told the driver. Maureen squeezed my hand for a long time. I watched her walk unsteadily up the steps to the front door. 'Second thoughts', I said, 'can you take me to

Piccadilly Circus. The Regent Bar.'

"The public bar was packed. A wide stairs was no doubt the way to the private bar. Even if it took all night, my mind was set. Five years I had waited and planned for this appointment. He had to be up there tonight, he just *had to*. I stayed downstairs, nursing my pint. I knew I'd need all my faculties to tackle Doyle. He was a hard man. That much I knew from way back. Always a dirty fighter. I didn't mind that in a street fighter, but there was no excuse for breaking a girl's nose and ribs and driving her to insanity and worse.

"When closing time was called I went out and stood at the bus stop where I'd have a clear view of the front door. Small groups began to trickle out. I stiffened. Three men had walked on to the street and stood chatting. After a few minutes two of them slipped around the corner, heading for Regent Street. The one left on his own was Doyle. The traffic stopped and Doyle moved briskly across to Piccadilly. I followed. Better let him go as far as possible from his friends, I thought.

"Doyle sauntered jauntily along Piccadilly, no doubt bent on a tour of inspection. He turned in to Bond Street and I quickened my pace. Bond Street was a quieter place for the business in hand. Slowly I overtook him, then suddenly whipped him around and brought him to a halt. Not a word was spoken. We stared, eyeball to eyeball. It had to be real close. I knew Doyle's first reaction would be the head. Doyles head went back. I leaned and took one step backwards simultaneously. With all the force I could muster, I brought my right foot under his crotch. He reeled on to the road. A small crowd was now gathering. Doyle slowly got to his feet. He straightened himself and came forward. A straight left grazed my temple. This was followed by a right, well below the belt. A long fight was out of the question. The police are never far away in the West End.

"Four or five times Doyle tested my guard with his straight left. Then, like lightning, his right foot came up. This was what I expected. I lifted my knee, not a split second too soon. His body lunged forward with the impact of his effort. My head went crashing home, straight between his eyes. He reeled on his feet, then went staggering towards the large plate-glass window. I grabbed him by the hair and lashed his head through the window. I wanted to kill him. That's what I had lived for all this time. I lifted my leg and brought my heel down on his ribs. The bastard would now know what broken ribs were all about.

"I raised my leg to crush in his other side, but someone grabbed me from behind. Without looking around, I crashed my head backwards. Nobody, just nobody, was now going to stop me finishing Doyle. A sharp blow on the back of my head sent stars dancing before my eyes. Vaguely I heard the familiar shriek of the black maria, *and the next thing I knew I was being bundled roughly on to the hard floor......*"

"Tell me one thing, Jimmy, did Doyle recover?"

"Let's say he survived," Jimmy answered. "After

a long spell in hospital, he went back to Dublin. The neighbours all think he got a stroke in England."

"And so he did, Jimmy," I said, "and so he did".

As the barman shouted 'time', Jimmy jumped to his feet, grabbed his pint which had remained untouched, and downed it without taking a breath.

"Please, Jimmy," I pleaded, pulling him back on the chair, "how about Maureen?"

"I'm sad to say poor Maureen did not survive. The very night I left her home, she took a massive overdose. Her friends found her unconscious when they returned early next morning. They got her to hospital, but it was too late."

T HE small block of flats seemed to grow like a mushroom. Already on the top floor, Jimmy was putting the finishing touches to the brick casing of the water tank.

"Have you that flag made?" he said to the hodsman.

"Can't you see I'm working at it," the hodsman shouted back.

"He's an optimist", my new job mate Dan Lunn remarked.

"Why the flag, Dan?" I asked.

"An old tradition," he replied. "When the chimney is built a flag is nailed up. The boss is expected to put up the money for the beer."

"Does it happen?" I asked.

"It seldom fails. It's considered unlucky to renege. More often than not when it's not paid, a few courses mysteriously disappear off the chimney the same night. No bricklayer in his right mind will replace them till matters are put right. Who wants seven years' bad luck?"

Willie,the hodsman, now had the flag ready, a discarded green pullover. "The right colour anyway," Dan said laughing. Willie was now busy gathering old newspapers and lunch papers from all over the floor. Pitching the lot into the tank-house he soon tripped up the ladder and disappeared inside, reappearing in a cloud of smoke. A round of applause came from everyone as Tommy emerged from downstairs. "Smart arses," he shouted waving a ten-pound note.

"The Guv' is no gobshite," Willie exclaimed to all round laughter, as the tools were quickly put away.

The gang was well into the second round before Tommy arrived. "You'll have it all to yourselves after tomorrow," he told Jimmy and Mickey Flynn. "I've managed to sort everybody out. I've got you fixed up in Ruislip for a couple of weeks," he told me. "After that, it's Foreign Service in Twickenham. Ah! not to worry," he said quickly, seeing my face drop, "you'll soon get used to moving around".

"You're a journey man now," Mickey Flynn remarked.

"RUISLIP," the bus conductor announced. 'Jack Collins will meet you at the bus stop,' Tommy had assured me. He didn't tell me the buses ran only every half hour. Having just missed one, I was now twenty minutes over the appointed time of eight o'clock. Jack Collins was either gone or, hopefully, hadn't yet arrived. When he didn't arrive on the next bus, I decided to start searching. Not far up the road, I shouted to a hodsman on a small site. "Must be further up the way," he replied.

After half a dozen such enquiries, I noticed a stack of bricks more than a hundred yards away in the middle of a field. Approaching, I could hear voices being carried on the breeze from behind the brickstack. Smoke rose a few feet to be whisked away in the strong wind. Already I was praying this forlorn outpost was not my destination.

Peeping around the corner, I was instantly spotted by the two men crouched over a miserable fire. Their conversation abruptly halted. One of them tipped the remains of his black tea-can over the fire and, standing up, moved without a word towards the footings. His companion grabbed a shovel and, splitting a bag of cement in two, lashed a few shovelfuls over a heap of mortar. Undecided what to do next, I plucked up courage and walked towards the man now busy on the trowel.

"Are you Jack Collins?" I asked.

"Jack Collins me arse!" he yelped, straightening up, a brick in one hand, a trowel in the other. His strange reaction caused me to burst out laughing.

"Hope you're not," I said impulsively.

"You cheeky hoor," he yelled, flinging the brick angrily back on the pile. The brick broke in two halves, narrowly missing his shins. Jumping sideways, he stumbled over the mortar board, landing unceremoniously on the wet bank.

I decided to make a hasty retreat. Turning, I saw the hodsman leaning on his shovel, almost convulsed with laughter. "Serves 'im right the silly blighter", the hodsman said, as I made to walk away. "Listen son, don't mind old Jack, 'is bark is worse than 'is bite."

"Tell you what," he went on, "take that 'atchet over to the 'edge and gather up a rake of firin'. I'll stick a can on and 'ave a drop-a-cha ready when you get back."

Highly confused, I looked over my shoulder. Now looking almost friendly, Jack Collins waved his hand in a forward movement, "Do what Bert says",he shouted. "We've lost enough time already."

Taking the hatchet from Bert, I threw the tools down and strolled towards the hedge. With Tommy Murphy in mind I decided I would see it through, at least for today.

"Jack Collins is my son-in-law," Bert confided, as he handed me the can of tea. "'ere," he said, "get stuck into that sandwich, the daughter gives us more than we need. I'll throw you a bit of mortar, on the back wall," he continued. "Just tear away and pass no remarks."

Throwing an odd glance in my direction, Jack sang quietly to himself for the rest of the day.

"**W**E'LL go for a pint," Jack announced as we cleaned the mud off our boots.

"'bout time you said something right," Bert replied, as we set out for the pub.

"You have an awful lot of songs," I said to Jack as we stood at the counter.

"Songs is right," Bert cut in. "There's at least 'alf a dozen Englishmen wiped out in every bloomin' song. Blimey, I'm surprised there's any left."

"They'll be one less any minute now," Jack threatened, "if you don't buy."

"The Bold Fenian Men....... stone the bloody crows," Bert moaned as he called the barman.

ARRIVING at the dance hall on Saturday night, I was greatly surprised to find Jack Collins in the hallway chatting with Tommy Murphy. Some funny story had obviously been told, as Jack, Tommy, another man I didn't know and a young woman were having a great laugh. My arrival set them laughing even more.

"Ah! there you are," Jack greeted me, "meet the missus."

"Me Dad has told me all about you," she said. "You'll be pleased to know you're the only Irishman he ever said anything nice about."

"The first time I got a bit of praise since I landed in England," I told her. "By the way, thanks for all the nice sandwiches".

"Oh! you can thank me Dad for them as well."

"Seems to me you had a right holiday out in Ruislip," Tommy Murphy quipped.

"You can be sure of it," said I, taking an admiring look at my left hand. The tips of all four fingers

and the thumb were neatly bound with tape.

"Come on," Mrs Collins invited, "you can buy me a cup of coffee. Me Dad is right, slave drivers every one of them."

Soon afterwards Jack Collins and the other man joined us at the counter.

"By the way," Jack said, "this is Michael Coleman, your next gaffer, a Kerryman too, God help us."

"Ballyheigue side," Michael said, as we shook hands.

S ETTLING in at Twickenham was far easier than I had feared. The cool, unruffled attitude of Michael Coleman made all the difference. He never raised his voice above a whisper, and was always friendly and helpful. The response to his unique brand of supervision was remarkable.

"Did you ever build a manhole?" he asked. I shook my head. "No time like the present to learn and no better man than Jock to show you how".

A very old man, Jock McKenzie was manhole king. He never took the pipe from his mouth, even when he was talking. The strange sounds that, now and again, emerged through the smoke, to all intents and purposes, might as well have been Chinese. His skill with a trowel,however, needed no words. After I had six courses built on a manhole, Jock would follow up to do the benching, kneeling on his cap in a cloud of smoke. I couldn't wait to see the outcome. Strange how a really good tradesman can leave his mark on something few people would ever see. The intricate curves shone like silver, not a trowel mark to be seen. The channel was as clean as new. Jock puffed on his pipe, waiting patiently for me to get out of his way at the next manhole. Rarely would Michael Coleman appear, then only to swap a joke with Jock, leaving me mesmerised at the ease with which they conversed.

FROM day one Michael found a seat beside me on the bus home. To my great surprise he confided he was interested in one thing above all else: to return to Ireland and buy a farm. To this end he would work all the overtime possible.

Going home on the bus one Friday night he surprised me by asking if I'd be interested in making a few quid on Saturday afternoon.

"What's the story?"

"Ireland are playing England tomorrow in the rugby International," he said, "you must know that. The traffic out here will be ferocious. I'm opening up the site for parking. The mixer driver and myself are having a go and we need another helper."

"You're on", I said. "How much do I get?"

"We're charging two shillings a car. You'll get sixpence a car, but you'll have to stay till they're all off the site and watch everything."

By three o'clock on Saturday we had two hundred cars stacked away. Had there been room we could have had two hundred more. The roars from the ground were deafening. The stand blocked our view from the site so that we were in the dark as to who was winning. In the dark, that is, until the first car owner arrived.

"Did we win?" Michael asked a dapper fur-coated man, a green and white hat covering his head and ears and a huge green and white scarf dangling about his knees. His gloved hand appeared from it's hiding place to momentarily remove the scarf from beneath his nose.

"Beaten by a lousy point," he barked. "Nine points to eight."

"Shocking altogether," Michael said, as he held the car door open, then nodded at me to get busy with the onrush of highly elated blue-bedecked customers.

The two weeks' wages tucked away in my pocket, for an afternoon spent sprinting between the cars to keep warm, helped greatly to ease the blow of Ireland's defeat. My spirits were high as I sat with Michael on the bus home.

"Keep your mouth shut on Monday," he warned.

"Mum's the word."

Mrs Williams understood when I explained I had to move nearer the job. The new digs in Chiswick would give me an extra hour in bed. No other lodgers were kept, but the digs cost thirty shillings - a bit pricey, but a good bit cheaper on fares.

"**W**E'RE starting a club", Michael Coleman said. "Well, a Christmas Club," he explained, "for anyone who wants to go home. It's ten bob a week and most of the lads are giving up the drink. They're all mad to get on that boat for Christmas."

"My digs are very dear," I said, "but I'll take a chance. Do you think will the job last that long?"

"Well," he said, "anyone who gets laid off or leaves will get their money there and then. The timekeeper will bank it all."

"It's one great scheme, whoever thought it up," I said. "I'm lucky as I have that money since the match and a few more bob, so I won't be stuck".

"It should be some crack on that boat," Michael said.

"With that mad shower? We'll be lucky if we're not all in irons before we reach Ireland."

"Not a hope," he said, "no drink till we're on the boat".

"You're a born optimist," I said, "but I like you".

"You're only saying that," he said, "because you know there's another match next week."

Chapter Three

IT was weeks now since I had been out to Murphy's in Willesden. I knew Tommy and the missus wouldn't be a bit pleased. God only knew how Colette Logan was getting on in Tipperary. If she had come back, somebody would have sent me word. I made up my mind to go to Willesden on Saturday night and get digs with somebody for the weekend.

"I've asked Frank Coffey to stay behind on Saturday," Michael Coleman said. "We have more room and there will be even more cars than last time."

Coffey was another of Tommy Murphy's proteges. From Westport, Co. Mayo, he had been in England since leaving school.

By two-thirty the whole site was packed to capacity. Coleman had upped the parking fee to two and six. "No danger of falling behind with the Christmas Club anyway", he said, as he handed Frank and myself ten pounds each in half crowns.Frank was going to Willesden too. We arranged to meet in the Spotted Dog at eight o'clock and then go to the dance. We couldn't have been more excited if we were going home.

Jimmy Palmer was at the bar with another man, and by the time we had downed a few pints and made our way to the dance hall, the place was packed.

Tommy Murphy appeared from nowhere. He grabbed me by the lapel and drew his fist back in a mock pose.

"Ah! don't hit him," Jimmy pleaded. "One belt and you'd be up for manslaughter."

"Wait till my missus gets her hands on him," Tommy said, "boys oh! boys."

But when we arrived in Tommy's place after the dance Mrs Murphy had gone to bed.

"Don't mind that fellow," she assured me next morning. We were in the kitchen, the sun shining through the big french window. "Have a look at the far corner of the garden. Wait till I open the window."

"A niche..." I whispered.

"A young fellow from Leitrim, Jerry Fitzsimons," she continued. "He's a year before you. Had a year in Tech."

"I must go down close and study it up", I said.

"Yes", she said, "I've told Tommy, nobody is pulling that niche down. I'm getting a nice statue and Jerry is going to build a pier to hold it."

"You're dead right," I agreed, "it would be a crime to pull it down."

"The things that man of mine has destroyed over the years is a caution," she said. "this time he's over-ruled."

"This Fitzsimons knows his stuff," I said, "hope to meet him sometime." Back of my mind I could not help feeling jealous.

"He has his mind made up to go home for good at Christmas. He's out of his mind about a girl at home and she won't come over here."

"Talking about girls," I said, "what about Colette?"

"She never misses a week without writing. To tell the truth she's not happy. She's very cross with you, I must tell you that. Anyway, I keep telling her that you are cross with her too. I think she likes that."

"I will definitely write this week," I said. "You know we are all going home from the job at Christmas. Whatever happens, I've made up my mind to visit Colette."

"I know for sure", Mrs Murphy said, pouring out another cup of tea, "that would make it the happiest Christmas of her life. I must get them two heathens out of that bed," she continued, making for the stairs. "We'll be barely on time for last Mass."

I slipped out to the hallway of the church during Communion and bought a silver decorated prayer book and a rosary beads blessed by the Pope. I kept them hidden until Jerry and I were leaving. I knew Mrs Murphy would cherish a gift like this. I slipped the tiny parcel into her hand in the hall and said in a whisper, "not to be opened for ten minutes."

"You're a scoundrel," she whispered back.

"Don't forget," Tommy said, "and this is an order. Get there how ye will, but be at the Union meeting tomorrow night."

"That's a promise, Tommy", we both answered, as we waved goodbye.

The small hall was packed as Jerry and I took our seats beside Frank Coffey near the door. "As you are aware, brothers," the Chairman, Snowy

Curtis, was saying, "the first item on the agenda is nominations for a new Branch Chairman and committee."

"Mr Chairman," the Cardinal was on his feet before the Chairman could sit down, "I wish to nominate brother Davis. I consider, Mr Chairman, that you have lost the confidence of all decent-minded members. Week after week you have allowed, and even encouraged, Communists and their hangers-on to dominate our discussions."

"I'm now vacating the Chair," Snowy announced. "The vice-Chairman, brother Potts, will take over."

"All those in favour of brother Davis for Chairman," Potts demanded. The Cardinal and two companions raised their hands. Almost everybody in the two front rows did likewise. "That's Mosley's followers," Frank whispered.

"If the tellers have done, we will now have a show of hands for brother Curtis."

The tellers handed a note each to the vice-Chairman. "Order, brothers", he said in a loud voice. "For brother Davis seventeen votes, for brother Curtis fifty three."

A great round of applause greeted the result. When silence returned and Snowy was back in the chair, the Cardinal jumped to his feet. "Mr Chairman," he shouted. "This meeting has been engineered by the Reds. This is a sad day for our Union." Frank dug me in the ribs. "Let's go," he said. "That eejit would give an aspro a headache. If he went on like that back home, they'd throw him into the nearest boghole. They wouldn't have too far to go naither."

"To tell you the truth," Jerry interrupted,"I think he's great crack. Mad as a coot. It's these other boys I have my knife in. Mosley's stooges. The Cardinal only hates the Reds. Those other bastards try to stir up the shite against everybody. Paddies, Jews, Blacks, Taffies."

"I'd say he'd be a good hand at building a niche," I said.

"By all accounts," said Frank, "he couldn't build a *ditch*."

We were still laughing when we reached the Spotted Dog.

"A letter for you," the landlady, Mrs Hopkins, said, as I arrived home on Friday night.

"My mother's handwriting," I told her. "Her letters are always full of news, so I'll read it upstairs. With all the moving I haven't had a letter for nearly a month."

"John and I are going out," she went on. "His sister isn't well so we have to go to Battersea. I'll give you my key, in case we're late."

The letter began: 'It breaks my heart to have to tell you, poor Gran passed away on June 1st. It was a great shock, as she gave no warning at all. She was working up to the end and had just finished a beautiful dress for Aine......'

I could read no more, unable to suppress the tears. Poor Gran. How kind she was, gentle and kind. All those nights I sat with her, the Singer sewing machine buzzing away, Gran stopping only to help me with my exercise or the spelling of some difficult word. I remembered her stories about her childhood; the daring exploits of her father and brothers, all dedicated to the struggle for Independence; her stories of fear and anguish when her three sons were engaged against the Tans and, worse still, the terrible Civil War. How proud she was of their heroism.

More than anything, I had been looking forward to seeing Gran at Christmas.

For a long time I lay on the bed. It was too late now to keep my appointment with Frank Coffey, even though this news would make one feel like getting drunk. How many times had people in Listowel said to me, "your Gran is a real lady." The neighbours who were on 'the other side' during the Civil War all came to her (when the shooting stopped) with their orders for confirmation and communion clothes.

On more than one occasion her windows were riddled with bullets. Such was the bitterness of the time. One thing is certain, the bullets were not aimed at Gran. In full measure, she too put the sad bad days firmly in the background. The house was once again a meeting place for all the neighbours, as well as being a Mecca for traditional musicians and stepdancers from near and far. How often had she told the story of my request, when I was about five years old, that she would give the Singer sewing machine to my mother when she died. It was the machine she had purchased the day she arrived in Convent Lane,Listowel, a very young bride. Over the years she had turned out garments of beauty and style for young and old. When praise was heaped on her efforts and skill, she would say, "Well if a job is worth doing it's worth doing well....."

Chapter Four

"**B**LOODY English weather." Michael Coleman was gazing at the sky.

"There's a right gambling school in the canteen," he said. "This rain can't last."

"Stick on the can," Frank Coffey said. "I'm making my fortune here." He was holding the bank at the pontoon school and his cap was well filled with his winnings.

"Brothers," Jock Denver, the Federation delegate, spoke from the door. "After the tea-break, there's a site meeting. It won't take long so we want everybody to attend."

"What's it all about?" I asked Frank.

"Don't know," Frank said, "but Jock never calls a meeting unless there's something important."

About three hundred men were assembled from all parts of the site, Jock Denver in the middle on a lorry flanked by seven or eight stewards.

"A meeting took place on Sunday last," he commenced, "of all Federation stewards from the South and West London areas. The main item on the agenda was the proposed march by Mosley and his blackshirts to the East End next Saturday. As you are aware, Saturday is the Jewish Sabbath and this is a calculated provocation and a deliberate attempt to confuse and divide the workers of this city. If Mosley gets away with this, his next move could well be a march on Willesden or Camden Town to sort out the Irish."

"Hear, hear!" a general round of applause.

"The stewards unanimously agreed to call on all

trade unionists to answer Mosley in the only language he and the fascists understand - action. We propose to join with the workers of the East End in a massive counter-demonstration. We propose to do what the government has deliberately failed to do, sweep these vermin off the streets. We propose to stand four-square against Mosley and his uniformed paid thugs. Cut short his attempts to split the working class and then knock us off at his leisure. Big men in high places are behind Mosley. The Tory press and politicians are blatantly condoning his every move. Whatever your nationality, whatever your religion this struggle concerns you."

A thunderous round of applause greeted Jock's final words.

"There must be millions of people down here," I said to Frank, "what are they expecting? The Germans and the Japanese?"

"Worse," he said, "by all accounts."

From the viaduct on the East India Dock Road, where at least a hundred and fifty from our job were assembled, we had a panoramic view. Thousands of tiny houses with their tiny chimneys stretched away for miles in all directions. Everywhere there were hordes of men and a goodly sprinkling of women, some very young. A band played in the distance. Jock emerged from the crowd, climbed on to the iron parapet and through a megaphone called for order.

"We would ask you from now on to take orders from the stewards. Mosley and his so-called army are on their way. We are well prepared and determined to send them packing. The Fascists had hoped to surprise our people from the rear, but they have been foiled. This area is vital and must be held. Long live the solidarity of the working class." A great cheer came from all those within earshot.

Jock, Jimmy and their companions were about to move off when three police officers appeared from nowhere. Speaking through a megaphone, one of them spoke to the stewards in particular and to all those on the viaduct in general. "This viaduct must be cleared. We must warn all concerned that obstructing the King's highway is a major offence. You have been warned."

Once again Jock climbed on to the parapet. "Listen carefully," he said in a loud clear voice. "More than a thousand fascist thugs armed with heavy cudgels, banner staffs spiked with nails, iron bars and the rest, are heading this way. If they get through here, a whole Jewish community of men, women and children will be completely at their mercy."

Almost before he had finished speaking, the clear voice of the police officer could be heard. "We repeat our warning. We call on you to disperse and clear the highway. We have our duty to do."

An eerie silence fell on the vast crowd and the bands ceased playing. A girl of about twenty left a group of about fifty other girls, displaying a banner 'London Students against Fascism'. Climbing on the parapet, she had barely commenced to speak when a great yell rose from the crowd. From a warehouse complex, a hundred yards away, about twenty mounted policemen suddenly emerged. Close behind, like magic, lines of police with riot shields came pouring out. Screams, shouts and more screaming came from all sides. All hell seemed to break loose. Hundreds had jumped on to the parapets, as horses, police and people were locked in a pitched battle.

"This is crazy," Frank shouted at me as we climbed on to the parapet. "If we even had a banner", he said, "we'd have some chance."

A mounted policeman swung his horse in a crazy circus-like circle in front of where we stood. More people seemed to be lying on the ground than standing. A violent blow on the knee cap knocked me sprawling. Stars danced before my eyes, then there was peaceful oblivion.

THE white mound before my eyes was the first thing I saw, then a cable from the ceiling. I had a massive thirst and a blinding headache. The man to my right was visible only in outline, his head covered in bandages. On my left, a man slept deeply.

"A cup of tea, that's what the doctor ordered." The nurse was standing beside the bed.

"That doctor is a genius," I managed to croak. "Where am I, nurse?"

"London Hospital," she answered. "All the hospitals for miles around are full. This country is gone mad. Pray tell me, how did you get yourself involved in this crazy business?"

"Long story. My God, nurse," I said, "did you say London Hospital?"

"That's right."

"That's just too much of a coincidence. Tell me," I said, "do you know Nurse Callaghan, Deirdre Callaghan?"

"Only to see. She's a year behind me. She's in the Madame Curie Ward down the corridor."

"Please, nurse," I said excitedly, "do find her when you get a chance and tell her I'd like to see her. I'll bring you a present back from Ireland when I go over at Christmas."

"Promises, promises," she laughed, as she disappeared through the swing doors.

The condition of my knee and the still throbbing headache made me realise that work would be out for some time. If work was out for any length of time, then, it was certain, so was my trip home at Christmas. All this was of minor consequence compared with the fact that Deirdre was just down the corridor. How would she react? I remembered the excitement and thrill of our date at the Vauxhall Bridge Road, that never-to-be forgotten run-in with the law, over a year ago. How stupid I had been to fall so quickly for Eileen's charm. How could I have forgotten to keep my date with Deirdre at Speaker's Corner?

"GOT news for you," the nurse startled me out of my thoughts. "The law has been around,

resumed with Deirdre.

The young day nurse came back, and now I was well enough to notice her red hair. "Mind if I call you Ginger?" I asked.

"When none of the 'heads' are around it's okay," she replied. She was checking the casualty list. Not one of the names I gave her was on it.

"Could be taken anywhere," she said,"or maybe they were all luckier than you..."

A penny for your thoughts," the voice said. I turned my head to find Deirdre sitting at the bedside. "My God," I said, "am I glad to see you!"

"How's the knee?"

"Forgotten all about it. Never bothers me. With all the comings and goings I forgot to ask you about your brother."

"Oh!" she said. "Believe it or not, Tommy has joined the R.A.F. Out of his mind to be a pilot."

"Fancy that!"

"The old man is doing his nut and Mother is worse. 'To think that a son of mine...', she goes on, 'blah, blah'...."

"I know the form, anyway maybe one day he'll go back to Ireland and start his own Air Force."

"Any news about your friends?" Deirdre asked.

"Not a word. The papers and radio are still going on about the big battles on Saturday. I must get you to ring the Spotted Dog and get word to Tommy Murphy that I'm here."

"I'll do that tomorrow," she assured me.

Our night nurse came in accompanied by a

young woman and an older man and woman. The nurse greeted Deirdre as they passed.

"That's the father and mother of a patient at the end of the ward," Deirdre said. "He lost a leg in a building accident three weeks ago and has been very ill. The girl is his wife. They're all from Clare. Some friends of his came in the other night and he played the fiddle for them. It was sheer magic."

"Can I let you in on a big secret?" I said.

"Oh! yes", Deirdre said eagerly.

"You are the only one in this hospital who can make a good cup of tea."

"Well, I'll let you in on another secret," she whispered back. "You're the biggest liar in this hospital. What happened your last servant?"

"It's a good job the night matron is off," she said, as she returned with the tea. "That's the lady will put manners on you all for the rest of the week. I'll tell you something. It depresses me to see how many Irish lads wind up here in casualty. It beats me how many of them get into trouble."

"Maybe it's trying to live up to everybody's image of us," I suggested. "The fighting Irish."

"They never seem to carry on like that back home," she said.

"Too many people know them at home, that's the difference."

"They know the girls back home too," Deirdre went on, "yet the girls don't make such fools of themselves over here. Look at yourself," she went on. "Sure, you're a walking disaster. You should join the monks."

"Never stick that," I said. "Men's company all the time. Totally unnatural. Just have to take my chances in this big bad world, even though the women cause so much trouble."

"If you say another word about women," she said, "I'll break the other leg. The only women we get in here, apart from accident calls, are battered wives and rape victims."

"I suppose the Paddies are blamed for most of that too," I said.

"I think the fault is fairly evenly spread," she concluded. "I worked in that unit for a year and boy was I glad to get away from it."

Suddenly the sound of the fiddle came from the far end of the ward: 'The Derry Air'. More poignant than ever that beautiful air could ever have sounded before. Eerie and beautiful. Twice more, within the hour, the same trance-like feeling banished completely the reality of our surroundings. He played 'An Cualinn' and, finally, 'Roisin Dubh'.

The music stopped and there was a long silence. Opening my eyes, I caught a glimpse of a large group of nurses who had been drawn from the nearby wards.

The sound that followed within minutes brought reality back with a vengeance. Deep sobbing came from the bedside where, so lately, there had been great music. Deirdre slid quickly towards the small group around the bed. The staff nurse and the doctor hurried to join her. The priest, fully robed, made his way past. Soon the prayers came wafting, responses coming from a number of voices around the ward.

T HE sun was beaming through the high window at my back as I came slowly out of a deep sleep. Ginger came breezing in. "Still on the night shift?" she quipped.

"Give us a couple of aspros, Ginger, and I'll marry you when I get back the use of my legs."

"If I ever marry," she retorted. "*If* I ever marry, it won't be to an Irishman. They're all mad. Cuckoo."

"I'll marry you nurse." The voice came from the man on my left. These were the first words spoken by him in three days. Up to now the curtains around the bed had been closed.

"Must be great to have the bandages removed," Ginger said.

"You can believe it," the new voice replied. "Couldn't tell until this morning if the operation was a success. Where's the champagne?"

"That'll come later," Ginger said. "Meantime here comes a nice cup of tea."

"Get that broken leg in the big schmozzle?" my neighbour enquired.

"Right," I replied.

"Blimey, it was just the luck of the draw, where those cudgels landed. I live in Whitechapel. Only for the huge turnout we'd surely have been massacred. My brother was in last night. He told me they've been celebrating Mosley's Rout with bonfires all over the East End."

"Good for them," I said, "pity we're missing all that."

A strange-looking man, all in black, with a heavy black beard emphasising the overall blackness of his appearance, came over and sat between us. He spoke to my friend in a language obviously familiar to both.

"Forgive us for speaking Yiddish," the all-black figure said, turning to address me. "We never use our language when we're in the company of gentile friends. I'm the local Rabbi. Our people down here have much to be thankful for. What part of Ireland are you from?" "Kerry," I replied.

"It's my ambition to go there for a holiday some time," he said.

"Keep away from Kerry then," Ginger had overheard his last remark, "they're all mad in that place."

"Ginger wants to marry me, Rabbi," I said, "can you perform the ceremony for us?"

"No problem."

"Thank you very much Rabbi," Ginger said. "I'll keep you in mind when the time comes, but I guarantee it won't be a Kerryman."

"**G**OT your message," Frank Coffey said. "Couldn't get here any sooner." He had his arm in a sling and a lovely black eye.

"Managed to get away in the crush. I saw you tumbling off the parapet, but I was powerless to do anything. What's the damage?"

"A big thing of nothing," I said. "Just a waste of time, precious bloody time at that. What's the news?"

"Jimmy, Jock Denver and Snowy were arrested, hundreds of others as well of course. The papers are full of rubbish. They're lumping the Fascists and the Communists together. Calling for the full rigour of the law. It would make a cat sick."

"You're worse to be reading that crap," I said. "You know as well as I do what it was all about. Any word about the job?"

"I'll call out tomorrow," he said. "I hope to be back to work in a few days. I got a right skelp on the knuckles, but nothing broken. You know.." he went on, "won't it be great to get on that boat next Christmas. I'll stay at home at least until the end of January." "Which January is that?" I enquired.

"You could be right there too," he said uncertainly. "This country is getting beyond a joke."

"Tell Michael Coleman to keep my job warm," I said. "Can't imagine how he's coping without me."

"Distracted, I'm sure," he agreed, "especially with me absent as well. "Tell Ginger I fancy her," Frank said, as he made to leave, " unless you're chasing her yourself."

"I'll put that right for you, take my word," I replied. "Maybe we could get her on that Christmas trip....? We'll try the dance in Cricklewood for starters!"

Chapter Five

A month is a long time to lie up when one is impatient: valuable weeks with no money going into the kitty for that all-important Christmas trip. Mrs Murphy insisted on making the long journey to the hospital twice a week. She took a great shine to Deirdre and Ginger, insisting that both should visit her at the first opportunity.

"The good news first," I told her as she arrived one Wednesday afternoon. "Doctor says I can go on Saturday morning. The bad news, I will need crutches for at least six weeks."

"Ah! what's six weeks?" she scolded. "Now, you picked the right day for getting out. There's a group over from Ireland, five musicians and two all-Ireland dancing champions, a girl and a boy. They're performing at a big festival in Dagenham tomorrow. Then on Saturday they're going to the dance and coming over with Tommy afterwards. You make sure Deirdre and Ginger come along."

About a dozen people were in Murphys' huge living room when I arrived with the two girls. Mrs Murphy insisted we take something to eat.

"When that gang gets here," she said,"they'll be starving."

"Some friends to meet you boys," Mrs Murphy said, as we entered the dining room. I nearly dropped the crutches. Looking up from the table, a big smile on his face, was George Logan. The two men with him I hadn't seen before. Both of them were huge. All three stood up and invited us to be seated.

"This is Steve Casey," George said, "and this is an American friend of Steve's, Rex Conway, better known as the Cincinnati Strangler."

"I'll give you a tip, boys," I told them, "don't cross swords with Ginger. Plenty of men in the city of London have tried, and they all came off second best."

"Never try besting a ginger-haired woman," George said, brushing his hand through his own tangled red mane. It was great to see him sober and so relaxed. If only poor Colette were here to see him!

"I was in your company a few times, George," I said, "but you were too busy to notice me."

"Busy?" he said, looking puzzled.

"Well, with your friends," I said.

"Yeah," Rex drawled, "and I bet a few that weren't so friendly."

"Could be right there," George agreed. "Could be right there, sure enough."

"Colette and I are good friends," I continued.

"Oh, I remember you now" George said, "I remember well. Colette is a topper. A topper."

"She sure is, "I agreed.

"Boss you all over the place, the same Colette," he went on. "Boss you all over the place."

"She'll make a great wife for some fellow," he continued. "A great wife. Damn me, but I miss her something wicked. Something wicked. I didn't think she'd stay at home so long."

"She writes every week," Mrs Murphy said. "Always a long letter, enquiring about everybody."

"Well, if she won't come over here," Steve remarked, "then we should all go over there and see her."

"Now you're talking Steve," Mrs Murphy said. "Seems to me everyone is arranging to go home at Christmas. Time we made our minds up."

A big commotion came from the hall. "That's them," Mrs Murphy announced.

Tommy entered, followed by about eight others. Everybody stood up to make room for the newcomers at the table. Two of them carried in crates filled with drink. They were introduced as Jack Flanagan and Jerry Fitzsimons - the same Jerry who had built the niche in the garden. Tommy took a bottle of whiskey from each of his two coat pockets.

"Must be intending to make a night of it," Rex drawled.

"You're joking," Tommy quipped. "That's just a small drop of medicine for George and myself. The rest of ye can drink tea."

"Have that bit of grub," Mrs Murphy said. "The rest of our friends out there will think we're gone to bed."

Mrs Murphy cleared some ornaments from the sideboard. "Up there with you," she ordered me, "and keep that leg out of harm's way."

I managed to get Deirdre sitting beside me. "Don't you dare to talk to any of those cowboys," I whispered. "Too many covetous eyes floating around here tonight."

"Some fine looking fellows," she retorted.

"Wouldn't you say Rex or big Steve would be any girl's fancy?"

"Fine looking girls too." I replied. "Take a look at the legs on that all-Ireland dancing champion." A sudden dig in the ribs nearly had me off the sideboard.

The musicians commenced a medley of tunes. It was easy to see why they were picked to come to Dagenham. The uilleann pipes, fiddle, melodeon and flute combined to make the blood tingle, playing reels, jigs and hornpipes. A solo on the flute, a slow air, was followed without a pause by another medley of reels. The atmosphere grew more and more electric. A tray of drinks was put on the small table beside the musicians.

Tommy called for order. "A special treat," he said, "especially for those who missed the dance. Will you give a big welcome to All Ireland stepdancing champion Rory O' Connor and the illustrious Agnes O'Connell..."

A good space was made in the centre of the room, and they danced the blackbird, hornpipe, jigs and a two-handed set dance. Only once before had I ever seen dancing equal to this. Only one man in Ireland, I am certain, could equal or excel such a performance: the great Kerry maestro himself, Jerry Molyneaux.

Tommy grabbed the dining room table, lowered the flaps and placed it in the middle of the floor. The band struck up a hornpipe. Like a bird, Rory O'Connor was on the table. His spectacular exhibition of footwork and faultless timing caused almost uncontrollable excitement, ending in a frenzy of applause.

Now voices were raised on all sides for a song from Jack Collins who had slid in quietly during the dancing. "'The Snowy Breasted Pearl' for me, Jack," Mrs Murphy put in her claim.

"Nell," Jack said, "it would take a braver man than me to ignore that request."

For the second time that night, memories of childhood were aroused.

If to France or far off Spain
She should cross the watery main
To see my love again, the seas I'd brave
Ah! but since 'tis heavens decree
That mine she'll never be
May the son of Mary
Me in mercy save.....

"**T**HAT was a night and a half," I said, as we settled in the bus.

"Some people were in great demand."

"I noticed that right enough," Deirdre agreed.

"Cut it out, you pair," Ginger said. "Both of you are so smart, you're both miles off the mark. The fact is, I took a big shine to Rex and he took a big shine to me - I think anyway. We have a date for Wednesday night."

"How in heavens name did that happen?" Deirdre exclaimed, knowing how closely Frank and Jerry were paying attention to Ginger all night.

"That shook you," Ginger said, "who was last to leave for Mass?"

"Ginger," I said, "you're a thundering rogue."

"Put that in your pipe and smoke it," she said. "This is my stop, be seeing ye." In a flash she was waving from the street.

"Hope you didn't try any tricks like that," I said to Deirdre.

"Didn't get a chance, now, did I?" she replied.

"I must remember to organise a new digs today," I said.

"Well for starters, we'll go to my flat. You can get a sleep. After that we can have a look at what's advertised in the newsagents."

"What do you think of my paper-hanging," Deirdre asked, as we arrived.

"Smashing job."

"The fireplace in the living room is a sight," she said, "it's falling asunder."

"Tell you what, Deirdre, we'll get some bricks

and build you a new one."

"In your condition?" she said.

"Oh, don't you worry,I can manage that job sitting down. Besides, you can give me a hand."

"I swear to God, you're the biggest chancer ever left the shores of Ireland. I'm putting on the spuds now. After dinner, I'm going for a long sleep, on my settee in there. There's a key in the door on my side," she quipped.

"The cheek of you," said I. "Don't you think I need a sleep as much as you do?"

I was awakened by the sound of music somewhere near. The room was in darkness. Hopping on one leg, I found the switch and then sat on the bed, wondering what time it was. Deirdre put her head in the door.

"Some people are great company."

"My God," I said, "What time is it?"

"Only half past ten," she replied.

"Why didn't you call me, we were supposed to go looking for digs."

"An earthquake wouldn't get you out of that bed," she said. "Too late to go anywhere now. I went to the shop and got some nice apple tart. We'll have tea and listen to the radio."

"Can't think of a better way to spend the rest of the evening," I said.

"It's a good job there's no work tomorrow."

"Tell you what, honey," I suggested, "we'll take a run out to Twickenham and see how the boys are getting on."

"I'm on," she said, "should be lovely out there on the river."

"Wish I had a fishing rod, we might get a few trout."

"There's a shop at Charing Cross with everything to do with fishing", Deirdre said.

"Worth a try", I agreed.

T HE man in the angling shop was full of advice. He knew the river around Twickenham like the back of his hand. The rod was second hand and only half the price of a new one. With it we got a dozen flies that no fish could resist. Deirdre carefully manoeuvred the rod onto the bus, and off it again when we reached our destination.

More familiar with a poacher's gaff, I tried every cast I knew, and some I didn't know, all to no avail.

"Can I have a try?" she asked.

"Why not? Time I took a rest."

Within minutes the rod was nearly jerked from her hands. A shout of glee from Deirdre, as I showered her with advice.

"Give him plenty of line. Don't rush him. Draw him in nice and slow."

"How long more do we go on like this?" she shouted. "He's going to get away, I know he is."

"Patience," I said, "that's the key to success."

Ten minutes later the beautiful shining trout, all of two pounds at least, gave up the struggle. Carefully I extricated the fly from his mouth. Like somebody grabbing hot coals that had fallen on to the carpet, Deirdre held the trout for some seconds at arm's length, then with both hands threw it into the water, ten feet from the bank. She threw herself down, half laughing and half crying. Then, looking up at my disbelieving, stunned face, she said, "no way could we kill him. He put up a great fight to survive, you must agree with that."

"All I can say, honey, is this... if it was my ould fella you were with, you'd be straight in after that trout. Come on, we'll just make it before they knock off."

All the way to the job, I deliberately kept bemoaning the loss of our lovely trout. "Well it was *my* trout," she said with finality,"and I'm delighted he's back with his pals, so there. Tell you what, I'll go on to the hospital and ask for the night off. It won't be any problem as there's a stand-by arrangement."

"A first class idea," I said. "Besides, after a weekend like that, you'd be crazy to work all night."

"I'll get some grub," she said. "Try and get home around half-eight."

TRY and get home around half-eight..." The words kept ringing in my ears. Up to now I had looked upon my stay in the flat as the most temporary arrangement: the key in the door, her brother Tommy's clothes in the wardrobe. Maybe this was just a casual remark with no real significance.

It was too late to meet the gang. Michael was getting ready to leave. "By the look of things, that job will be finished before I'm rid of these crutches," I told him.

"Don't kid yourself," he replied. "There's another year's work at least. Another block of fifty flats and fifty more houses."

"That's good news," I said.

"There's your two back days," he said handing me an envelope. "The boys had a whip-round. That's in the envelope as well."

"I just don't know what to say."

"Come on", he said, "we have to see Frank Coffey in the local."

"Twenty quid!" I exclaimed, as I opened the envelope in the pub. "I wouldn't have that saved if I'd been working."

"We're starting Sunday work next week", Michael said. "The firm have agreed. All the money will be put aside for the trip."

"Give me a bottle of wine", I said to the barman, as we were leaving.

"I like it," Frank said. "Must have something to celebrate."

"That's the understatement of the century," I replied.

"**Y**OU'RE just in time," Deirdre said, as I arrived.

"Feast your eyes on that," I said, placing the bottle of wine on the table.

"Hope you like steak and kidney pudding."

"Hold on," I said, "till I give myself a pinch to make sure I'm not dreaming."

"Saw Ginger at the hospital. She's all excited about meeting Rex on Wednesday night. Steve and himself are involved in a big wrestling tournament at the weekend. Jack Doyle is making his debut as a wrestler."

"That should be a right bit of crack alright," I said.

"Wouldn't go near it. Anyway I'm working all over the weekend."

"Listen honey," I said, "that suits me fine. I don't want my girl getting too friendly with these glamour boys. Bad enough Ginger getting involved."

"She's welcome to them," Deirdre said emphatically. "Just a bunch of fly-by-nights."

"I love you"," I said, "and what's more, you're a great cook."

"Oh! yeah?" she said, pouring out the wine. "I told you already, you're a chancer."

"There's one thing you must admit, Miss. One thing you cannot deny. Will you agree with that, now tell me straight?"

"I swear to God you're going queer in the head. What are you talking about?"

"My brains," I said. "You must admit, I have great brains."

"Right now I'm fully convinced your mind is beginning to stray. Whatever you drank in the pub has definitely gone to your head."

"Well, do you want to know how I can prove that I am super intelligent?"

"You'd better come back to the hospital and get

the doctor to look at you. I'm certain now you got a blow in the head the day you got that knee smashed."

"You'll never make a good nurse, darling," I said. "Now, let me explain. I have figured out how two people can sleep in the one bed without ever touching ."

"A born genius, to be sure."

"Now, let me explain how this near miracle can be achieved. One person lies on the inside, the other person lies on the outside. The person on the outside places his knee, which is covered in plaster a foot above and a foot below the knee, right in the centre."

"Great brains altogether, I must admit. I have a better idea and I have no brains at all." She leaned backwards and turned the key in the door.

"The girl is mad," I said. "Just think of all the girls who would give their life savings to have a chance like that. A chance like that only comes once in a lifetime."

"Thanks be to God," she said. "Now will you stop blathering and tell me something interesting."

"Well, I'll tell you, I have one great ambition. One day I am going back to dear old Ireland. Over there, I'm gonna buy a breathtaking site on the side of a hill, with rolling meadows and beautiful trees stretching down to the sea shore. Right there on that site, I'm gonna build a small mansion, with yellow bricks. Twenty windows with a perfect arch over every one. A lovely porch; a huge living room with a window giving a panoramic view of the countryside; a small study, complete with stained glass window, crowned with a beautiful niche."

"I dream like that all the time, darling, but I usually wait till I get to bed. By the way, what's a niche?"

"I'll show you one next time we're in Murphy's," I said.

"You know, this mansion you want to build, don't you think there's enough places like that in Ireland already? If you ask me, it sounds more like a nursing home or a convent. My idea is a small cottage, miles from anywhere. Maybe I'd take up fishing as a hobby."

"Better not take it up as a living anyway," I said. "I'd hate to die with the hunger in that remote cottage."

"Let's finish off this wine," she said, "then I'm for a bath."

T O my great surprise, when Deirdre emerged from the bathroom she went straight to the bedroom. "I've decided to try that barrier idea", she announced through the door.

"Didn't I tell you, I'm the brainy one around here," I answered.

"Any nice bedtime stories?" she asked, as I got into bed beside her.

All the talk and all my efforts to appear calm and casual could not alter an overwhelming feeling of joy and happiness. "To tell you the truth," she whispered, "I'm very happy."

"Me too", I answered.

"Mansion indeed, some notions."

"Matter of fact, my love, you can keep your cottage as well. I've come to the conclusion, home was never like this."

"Now tell me that story," she said, as we embraced over the barrier...

"WE'RE having visitors tonight," Deirdre announced as she arrived home from work.

"Visitors?" I cried, "who have you invited?"

"Rex and Ginger. He's going back to America on Monday. I'm just falling off my feet so I'm not getting out of that bed till tea time."

"Just write out the list of shopping," I said, "and leave the rest to me."

"Take a firm grip on your seats," Rex advised, as soon as we sat down at the table. "Thought you two should be the first to know. Show them the evidence, honey." Ginger held out her left hand displaying her diamond engagement ring. All four of us broke into uncontrollable laughter.

"One thing is for sure," Deirdre said, "you Americans don't waste much time."

"Right first time," Rex said. "Especially when a chance of a lifetime comes our way."

"When's the big day?"

"Well I have to go back on Monday. We've seen the priest at the hospital and he's great. All the preliminaries should be sorted out in about four weeks. It's a big help that I'm a Roman Catholic. After we eat," Rex went on, "we want you two to come to the West End for a celebration."

"Steve has agreed to be my best man," Rex said, as soon as we were seated in the nightclub at Piccadilly Circus. "Have you asked Deirdre yet, honey?"

"I was about to", Ginger said. "The thing is, we want you to be bridesmaid."

"I'd be real mad if you asked anybody else," Deirdre replied.

"All settled," Rex said. "Now that calls for champagne."

"**A** few more nights like this and we'll never go back home," I told Deirdre.

"Speak for yourself," she retorted. "Nothing will ever change my mind about that cottage."

In his wildest dreams, Rex could not have imagined all the planning and organisation of the weeks before the wedding. Trips to the West End, discussions, fittings, invitations and more trips to the West End.

"Who would believe so much work goes into one wedding?" I said.

"Good crack," Deirdre said. "The girls in the hospital are just as excited as we are."

"I'll leave you to Ginger's place and have an early night," I said.

"Keep your fingers crossed," Deirdre said, as Ginger opened the door. "Don't forget to set the alarm clock."

THE scene outside Brompton Oratory came as a big surprise. Close as I was to all the planning and scheming of Deirdre and her friends, the sight that met my eyes amazed me. Twenty nurses in uniform lined up in two ranks to form a welcoming party. On the steps the children's choir from Willesden was already singing. Mrs Murphy and Tommy were there surrounded by so many familiar faces: Jerry Fitzsimons, Frank Coffey, Bill Ryan, all the members of the Ceili Band. In the background, head and shoulders over the rest, the red (now well combed) head of George Logan. Beside him was the biggest surprise of all: Jimmy Palmer, straight from Wormwood Scrubs.

There was a general buzz of excitement as Steve Casey, then Rex and behind him Jack Doyle, emerged from a taxi, half a dozen photographers surrounding the trio. Suddenly all eyes were turned, as Deirdre and Ginger emerged from the second taxi. They got a spontaneous round of applause, joined in by a large crowd, who had now gathered in the street. The famous Brompton Oratory had surely never witnessed a sight like this. How beautiful both girls looked. Only with great difficulty could the photographers be moved and a pathway made for them to lead the way into the church.

The ceremony over, there was another spell of photo taking until Father Danny emerged to rescue Ginger and Rex and lead the way to the nearby Park View Hotel. I looked at the towering figures of Rex, Steve and Jack Doyle, and the radiantly happy figure of Ginger, surrounded by her colleagues from the hospital, all anxious to get a closer view of her wedding outfit. Standing at the counter with Jimmy, it was all I could do to believe I was part of this gay affluent occasion. It was only my second wedding, and my mind was crowded with memories of that day in Listowel not so long ago when Uncle Dick and Madge, likewise gave scant notice of their momentous decision.

Jimmy interrupted my thoughts. "Meet one of my best friends", he said.

The tall man standing at the counter shook my hand, nodded vigorously, but did not speak.

"This is Blackie. Blackie O'Donnell," Jimmy continued, tussling Blackie's hair. The tall silent man smiled, making a playful pose with his clenched fist. "Blackie is a Donegal man," Jimmy went on. "He arrived here two years ago and had a great future in the ring. That weekend we were in the East End, he was top of the bill in the Vale Hall. The Hazleys had a boxer down from Glasgow. They ordered Blackie to take a dive. Big money involved. Blackie put your man away in the third round. They got him the next night leaving the gym. They left him for dead, but Blackie is tough. Aren't you, Blackie ould son?" Jimmy said, noticing Blackie was taking an interest.

"Oh! Aye," Blackie said, turning once again to gaze into his pint. Behind us the waiter suddenly rang the bell to indicate the meal was ready. Blackie whipped round instantly hunched into a fighting pose. Jimmy threw his arms around him, guiding him amidst great laughter to his seat in the dining room.

The meal was over, the hilarious speeches, and the songs; at last it was time for dancing. Now Deirdre was free from her duties as bridesmaid.

"A brilliant idea entered my mind when I was in that church," I told her, as we took the floor.

"Let me guess...You've decided to become a monk.." she said as she ran from the floor laughing and disappeared into the ladies toilet.

Too soon the time arrived for everybody to pour on to the road for the big send-off. With tears and shrieks, the nurses clamoured around Ginger and Rex. The taxi now scrambled away, an assortment of tin cans clattering behind.

"The end of a perfect day," Deirdre said, as we headed for home, sharing a taxi with Jimmy, Blackie and Michael Coleman.

"Jack Doyle and myself are organising a night for Blackie in three weeks time in the Vale Hall," Jimmy said. "We'll have a team over from Dublin. Tommy Murphy is running a dance as well. He won't be short of a bob, for the foreseeable future at least."

Chapter Six

"**F**IGHTING fit and ready for work," I told Michael Coleman. "How am I fixed for Monday?"

"The job is sound," he said. "I want a big favour, Michael," I whispered. "I told Deirdre some time ago I'd build a brick fireplace in the flat. I need fifty bricks and the cement and mortar. I'll do the job tomorrow. She's on days."

"As good as done," he said. "We'll load Gus up, he'll drop them round in the morning."

"Michael," I said, "you're one in a million."

To my great surprise, Jerry Fitzsimons arrived with Gus next morning on the lorry. "Just come to supervise the job", he said. "You make the tea, we'll pull out this Queen Victoria relic. Gus will dump the lot."

By one o'clock the fireplace was complete, with not even a mark on the new wallpaper. Well satisfied, we made the tea and sat down to admire our masterpiece. Hearing footsteps in the hall, we barely had time to look at each other. Deirdre's brother Tommy, looking startled, was standing in the doorway.

"Stone the crows," he said, "I thought for a minute I was in the wrong house. That fireplace looks good."

"Great to see you, Tommy," I said. "Deirdre wanted this fireplace done before you got home. We nearly left it too late."

"I should have written," he said. "I take it she's

working today."

My mind was working overtime. We were mad not to anticipate this. Deirdre had been adamant that Tommy's first leave was in September.

"Listen lads," Tommy said, " I arranged to meet the girlfriend in the Royal Oak at one thirty. We might be back before ye go."

"That's fine Tommy, we'll have the place all cleaned up."

"Can't get over the fireplace," he said, " and the new wallpaper."

"All Deirdre's work," I said , as he rushed out.

"Get that lump hammer, Jerry," I said, " and see could you knock my heart back into place."

"Your heart!" Jerry said.

Five minutes was enough to have all incriminating evidence cleared from the bedroom. Suit, shoes, shirts, the lot were all nicely bundled up in a half sheet of Deirdre's wallpaper.

"Let's try a fire in this thing," I suggested to Jerry, "and see how she draws."

"As Dan Lunn always said, 'if it doesn't draw smoke, it will draw tears'."

"Tears is right," I said, "Dan Lunn never said a truer word."

"Will you hold your whisht," Jerry said, "you're the luckiest hoor that ever left the bogs of Ireland."

"How right you are, mate,"I agreed, as the fire sprang into life. "No smoke, no tears," Jerry said.

Tommy arrived back with his girl friend, Gladys. Yes, we would all meet up before the end of his leave.

"Any friend you could bring along for Jerry?" I asked Gladys. "He's very shy with the girls."

"That's right," Jerry said, "especially good looking ones."

"Tell you what," Gladys said, "my friend is really beautiful and she loves Irishmen."

"Settled," Jerry said. "We'll all go to the dance in Cricklewood, Saturday night....."

"My God, I'm glad you rang." It was Deirdre's worried voice. "I'm in its here since Tommy phoned."

"Keep cool, love," I said,"everything worked out okay."

"What possessed you to bother with that fireplace?" she went on.

"Use your head sweetheart, only for that fireplace, I'd have been in bed."

"Of course."

"I'm going to Jerry's place to change, see you at the hospital at eight o'clock."

I just can't understand Tommy not writing," Deirdre said, as we settled in the pub. "What are you going to do?"

"Didn't I always tell you I was full of brains, didn't I?"

"You'd be looking for your brains," she said, "only for mother luck."

"Right," I said, "brainy and lucky. The thing is, darling, Tommy and Gladys won't be a bit lonesome on their own for the next week."

"Are you mad?" she cut in sharply. "No way

would Tommy bring Gladys into the flat to stay."

"Who said anything about her staying? Just tell Tommy you're going to keep Ann company for a few nights, seeing as Ann was so good to you."

"It won't work," she said. "Besides I'm on nights next week. Also you're going back to work Monday."

"There's no Act of Parliament says I have to, now is there? Besides,my love, this knee isn't half right and another week would do it all the good in the world."

"Some day your scheming will get you hung," she said. "Pray tell me, Your Brilliance, where does all this planning leave us?"

"Tonight you stay in the flat and I'll bunk in with Jerry. Tomorrow we find a room, that should be easy. All next week we spend visiting places of interest. Monday , The Tower, very interesting. Must see where Henry the Eighth disposed of his problems. Then there's the Museum on Tuesday. Crystal Palace on Wednesday. Madame Tussauds, etc.etc. Can't go back to Ireland at Christmas and not be able to talk about all these places, now can we?"

"I'm sure they can't wait to hear all that stuff, especially since they have a pain already, listening to returned yanks and returned cockneys."

"You please yourself, mate. As for me, I'm gonna descend on that there town and dazzle everybody with style and knowledge. I might even bring my tools and build a brick fireplace in the kitchen."

"I must go now," she said. "I'm dying to see our

new fireplace."

"I didn't do it all", I said, "but the best brickwork on the left-hand side is all mine and also the arch."

"We'll get a photograph taken on Monday," she said, "and when Tommy goes back, we'll put it on the mantelpiece."

A right gathering of the clans tonight," Deirdre remarked, as Ann led the way into the dance hall. "Don't look now," she continued. "There's Tommy, Gladys and her friend coming to greet us."

"Hi there," Tommy said. "Like ye to meet Shirley."

Gladys had said her friend was beautiful, and she was not exaggerating. Shirley was blonde, had a great figure and from the start was very friendly and cheerful.

"Where's this hunk Jerry I've been hearing all about," Shirley demanded to know.

"Don't worry," I said, "Jerry will be here, that's a sure thing."

"I've got my eye on Jerry as well," Ann spoke up.

"In that case," said Shirley, "you and I will have to toss for him."

"If I know anything, girls, I think the problem will solve itself. Jerry goes nowhere without his mate Frank Coffey and for my money, Frank is a far better catch than Jerry."

"Well in that case," Shirley laughed, " I'm keeping my options open."

Suddenly from the doorway, Jerry and Frank

came strolling in, followed by Jimmy, John and Peter Palmer.

"Ah, come on," I said to Deirdre, as Ann set about the introductions. "Let's test that knee out in this slow waltz."

"Poor Jerry and Frank," Deirdre said, "they're right back to square one. Only Rex came on the scene, they would surely be sworn enemies by now."

"Guess what," I said. "Take a glance over your shoulder."

Deirdre looked round to see Shirley dancing gaily with Jimmy.

"Well, if Jimmy gets his eye on her, it's bye, bye, birdie," I said.

"There's always Ann for them to fight over."

"How right you are," I agreed, "and a lot more good-looking Anns here tonight as well."

"Just forget about all those Anns," Deirdre said, as the waltz ended. "As far as I can see, the men here tonight outnumber the girls at least two to one.So keep your eyes off those Anns, I'm warning you."

"A bit of news," Jimmy whispered, as we got back. "Jock is getting out on Monday. Tommy Murphy sent word over, he has a few bottles in the back room. We'll all adjourn there, just to be polite."

"First one on me," Tommy Murphy said as we thronged into the makeshift bar. Bill Ryan was barman-in-chief.

"I've been appointed head lad," he said, "because

I'm the only one here with a cork-screw."

"There's a catch in the free drink," Tommy said. "I've asked the M.C. to announce that Jock Denver is being released on Monday. We're doing a whip-round, so you're all volunteers with the boxes."

"As good as done," Jimmy said. "It's doubtful if Jock will be fit for work for a few weeks anyway. Not after the treatment."

"Must tell you," Tommy said to me, "just in case you go missing again. I have you booked into the Tech. That means two nights a week, from September 1st. Your turn for the niche, that's one night a week." This information gave great amusement to the gang.

"By the way Tommy," I said, "can you think of anything I might do in my spare time?"

"Yeah", Tommy answered, "they haven't banned Trade Unions yet in this country. We meet once a week on Mondays....."

"How's the knee?" Michael Coleman said when I reported for work the next day.

"The knee is fine, Michael," I replied. "It's the rest of me that's not so good. To tell you the truth, I was hoping it would be lashing rain."

"You'll survive. Done any pointing?" he asked.

"An hour's lesson from Tommy," I said. "That's one thing I want to master."

"There's enough pointing to keep us going to Christmas," Michael went on. "Jimmy Smith is in charge of the squad and they don't come any better. Smithy's the shop steward, so better have a clear card."

"LISTEN love," I said to Deirdre, "would your friends at the hospital be interested in coming to Blackie's big night?"

"Boxing?" Deirdre said, aghast. "Are you losing your marbles? That's a man's game. And a stupid man's game at that."

"Ah! get away with you, you're away behind the times. Think of all those hunks coming over from Ireland. Everyone of them a ringer for Johnny Weissmuller."

"Yeah, and with about the same amount of brains," she retorted.

"Anyway, just forget about the boxing, we'll make it a big night out. Don't forget it's Blackie's big night."

"I know that , but it will be packed anyway."

"Bet you anything, Ann and Shirley will be all for it," I teased. "Take some tickets anyway, they're only a pound."

"How many does the place hold?" she asked.

"Well, my tickets are numbered 700-750."

"That's big money," she said.

"Maybe so, darling. Don't forget, fares have to be paid and a few more expenses. The hall is free and the referees are giving their services free as well, so now."

She took the tickets half-heartedly and said "I'll see what the rest of them have to say..."

WHEN Deirdre came home on Friday night she exclaimed; "You were right for once, that crowd on my shift are all mad. I think they'd go to a hanging if that was still possible. Makes you laugh you know. The healing profession, how are you!"

"I know," I said, "what you're telling me is, you sold all the tickets?"

"I'll want at least ten more. Two of the doctors are coming, and it wouldn't surprise me if Matron wants to come as well. Shirley is bringing a party."

"Boys oh! boys," I said, "but that's great news altogether."

"Most of them are coming to cheer for the London team," she said.

"Well, everyone keeps telling me it's a free country, so let them. Mind you, from what Jimmy tells me," I lied, "those Dublin boxers will dance all over them. He reckons they'll just ate them. You go to the Vale Hall any Sunday and it's Irishmen, Scotsmen or Welshmen, very few Englishmen."

"Maybe it's because Englishmen are more civilised," Deirdre said. "Or maybe they don't want to make money half killing each other."

"I'll tell you nothing but the truth," I said. "I don't like Englishmen, but I think the English girls are just great." A bedroom slipper hopped off the bathroom door, just missing my head, as I made my escape.

We had arranged to meet Ann and Shirley at Speaker's Corner later that night. They were already there when we arrived, standing on the outer edge of a large crowd and both looking really cross. "Somebody done something to you two?" I asked.

"Just have a listen to that one," Ann said. "Wouldn't I love to pull her off that rostrum."

A good-looking girl of about twenty-five with an Irish accent was dealing with a heckler. The heckler wanted to know if she made her living speechmaking or by some other profession.

"None of your business, the question has nothing to do with what I've been expounding."

He tried to rephrase the question, but was promptly shouted down by members of the audience.

"I repeat," the speaker said, addressing the audience once more. "Women in Ireland are nothing but slaves. Indeed, I am convinced that slaves had more security and were treated with more respect. At least their menfolk defended them to the best of their ability. Men in Ireland today have more respect for their cows or their horses."

"You're a liar," a man shouted. "Why don't you go back and say these things in Ireland?"

"I'll tell you why," she shouted back. "It's because over here, at least at Speakers Corner, there's only an odd ignoramus like you."

"Rape is more common here than over in Ireland," he shouted.

"How wrong you are," she retorted. "The majority of women in Ireland, having anything from six to sixteen or twenty children, are rape victims, whether you know it or not, or indeed, whether they themselves know it or not."

"Ah! get stuffed," another heckler shouted.

"You'll get your reward in heaven the priests tell them. The family is sacred. A woman who is raped once suffers for the rest of her life, physically and mentally. She can never fully recover. The majority of women in Ireland are raped, not once, but over and over again."

"Oh! I loike that", somebody shouted. "Tell us that bit againe."

"Raped," she continued. "Raped by their God-fearing, craw-thumping, ignorant drunken louts of husbands."

" 'ear, 'ear," a man shouted. "Down with the men. Down with the men."

This chant was taken up by about half the audience, as the speaker, her voice rising above the crowd, called out. "Women, we beg you, join with us, the Sisters of Hope."

" 'ope? No 'ope you mean. If I 'ad a sister like you, I'd drawn 'er," the man with the loud voice shouted above the din.

"Get off the stage," a man in a cultural accent shouted. "Disgraceful, disgraceful, above all things a woman should show some delicacy."

"Delicacy? Did you hear that, sisters? Delicacy! May God forgive you," she shouted, rolling up her notes and holding them above her head. "You go and tell that to women in the sweat shops over here. People like you make me sick. Sisters, you can collect our pamphlet outside the gate. Don't forget we are here next Friday, Saturday and Sunday nights."

"Let's go," Ann said. "I feel like a huge breath of

fresh air. Those hecklers would make you sick."

"We'll have to run for the pub," I said, "otherwise it'll be closing time." Breathless and laughing, I arrived last, badly handicapped by the bandaged knee. The three girls, mightily pleased with leaving me so far behind, mockingly set about assisting me through the door of the pub. The place was packed. All eyes seemed to turn on us, no doubt curious about the commotion. A small group of men stood close to the door.

"Stone the crows," one of them remarked loudly. "Must be Biddies night out."

"The guv' won't 'ave Biddies when 'es around," one of his companions said, equally loudly.

"Takes all sorts," another one went on. "Mind you, I wouldn't refuse the blonde if she asked a favour."

"Just let's go," Deirdre said pleadingly.

"Keep cool, girls," I whispered. With great difficulty, I made it to the counter, returning with three glasses of ale and a pint. It was obvious the girls were at the receiving end of more insults.

"Wish you hadn't bothered with those drinks," Deirdre said. "If there's one more insult, mine's going all over that shower."

"It's nearly closing time anyway. Just ignore them," I said.

"What's 'e got, then, that we 'aven't got?" the loud one seemed bent on continuing the aggro.

"Big balls. All Paddies 'ave them."

"Pardon me," somebody said behind me.

All three girls were looking somewhat

bewildered over my shoulder. Moving aside, assuming somebody wanted to pass, I too was suddenly transfixed.

"Don't look now," the loud one was addressing his companions. "Lady Galway and Co. are takin' a powder."

Four men dressed in exotic attire were moving towards us from the far side of the lounge. Our neighbours became very quiet. Actors, I decided, on their way from a pantomime. They came to a halt between us and our gibing neighbours. In spite of the exotic gear and lavish hair styles, all four looked dangerous and unpredictable. Only the untouched pint in my shaky hand persuaded me I was not in an advanced state of delirium tremens. The blonde man was over six feet, bronzed and fit looking, with a faint scar, two inches long, on his right cheek. His three dark-haired companions, also bronzed and tough-looking, stood behind him, taut and vigilant.

In a flash the blonde man grabbed the loud one by the collar. "Up to your tricks again, Gibson?" he said icily. "You and those poxy mates of yours, just never give up, do you?"

Tightening his grip on Gibson, he half turned his head towards us. "These guys just love insulting people, especially women. Isn't that right, Gibson?" he rasped.

"Didn't worry us," I replied, more than anxious to avoid being in the centre of a brawl.

"'aving a bit of a lawf," Gibson said.

"I know your idea of a lawf," the blonde man

mimicked. "You and your friends tried it once before, remember? Now piss off."

"We were going anyway," Gibson replied. They finished their drinks hurriedly and left without another word.

Turning to the girls, I was startled by the scared look on Deirdre's face. Her eyes were fixed on the blonde man as if she were hypnotised. He was donning a pair of kid gloves and shaking his head slowly from side to side.

"Deirdre Callaghan," he said. "I know you haven't a clue who I am, but I recognised you the minute you arrived."

Deirdre made no reply.

"Would the word 'Ranter' mean anything to you?"

"Ranter....." she stammered, "Ranter Casey. Ranter....I don't believe it. I swear your mother wouldn't recognise you, or your father either."

"I'm sure you're right, Deirdre," he said laughing. "You're the last person in the world I expected to meet. Don't worry, this gear will be well and truly discarded when I set sail for Ballycoloran."

"Have you taken up acting, Ranter?" she asked.

"In a way, my love," he answered.

His three companions began to laugh. "Best actor in London, that's what he is, Miss," one of them remarked.

"Let's move outside," Ranter suggested. "Away from this noise. Tell your friends and mine, Deirdre, how often I gave you a lift to school on my bike. This your bloke?"

"Right, Ranter."

He handed Deirdre a card. "Don't take any notice of the name," he said. "That's me alright. One thing before I go, Deirdre. Give me full marks for recognising you, seeing as you were only about ten when I left home."

"Full marks, Ranter," she said, as the four walked quickly away towards Belgravia....

One of the barmen was about to lock up. "Ask him for a bottle of wine to take away," Deirdre said. "Come back to the flat girls," she continued. "We could do with another drink after all that."

"You know Lady Galway, then?" the barman said.

"Comes from the same place I do," Deirdre told him. " Looks like he's doing well anyway."

"Bet your life," the barman replied. "Private Secretary and chief bodyguard to an Indian Prince. The three others are employed fulltime as bodyguards. Your friend Lady Galway is bossman in the Club. That's why Gibson and his pals bailed out so fast."

"If I live to be a hundred I'll never get over the shock." Deirdre had been very quiet since leaving the pub. "Ranter.... of all people."

"I know how you feel," Shirley said consolingly. "It's only when a close friend or a near relative turns out that way, the real horror is brought home."

"Those people just make me sick," I said emphatically. "They're just freaks. This country is crawling with them."

"This country is not unique in that respect," Deirdre said.

"Maybe not. But there's nowhere else where they're so brazen about it."

"You'd be surprised how many of these people wind up in hospital," Ann interjected. "Mostly victims of violence. Quite a few come in mentally disturbed, just nervous wrecks."

"Surely they have nobody to blame only themselves," I persisted. "Isn't it easy to see why ordinary people react like they do?"

"When you get to know those people, it's a different story altogether," Deirdre went on. "Usually they are model patients and mostly above average intelligence. Maybe you wouldn't be so prejudiced if you came up against this problem as we do."

"Prejudiced?" I said heatedly. "Am I prejudiced because I want to be natural?"

"Oh!" said Deirdre, "you're never done talking about that Cardinal in the Union and how prejudiced he is."

"What the hell has politics got to do with it?" I thundered. All three girls were laughing heartily at my irritation.

"All right for you two," Shirley said, jumping to her feet. "See you at Blackie's night in the Vale Hall. Maybe Deirdre and yourself can sort this thing out in the ring."

"We'll finish the wine," Deirdre said, when Shirley had left. "It will help us to sleep."

O UTSIDE and inside the Vale Hall was buzzing with excitement. Tommy Murphy, Jimmy

Palmer and half a dozen club officials, all wearing stewards' badges, were busy checking tickets and directing people to their seats. Mrs Murphy was sitting with Bill Ryan's wife on a bench seat in the foyer. "We've been appointed to the refreshment bar," Mrs Murphy said, as Deirdre joined them.

"Never so happy to volunteer for anything," Deirdre said.

"By the way", she said to Jimmy,"where is Blackie?"

"Between the two of us," came the whispered reply, "Blackie was taken into St Mary's Hospital this afternoon."

The M.C. in a booming voice, was introducing the six Irish boxers from the ring. Not yet togged out, they were waving to the huge crowd, all singing 'When Irish Eyes are Smiling'. Pandemonium broke out as Jack Doyle climbed in to the ring, waved to the crowd and joined in the singing.

Half a dozen women were already in the refreshment room, all eager to help,and glad to escape from the uproar and excitement.

"Never saw so many women in this hall before," Tommy Murphy said. "I'll put a couple of men on the door to make sure no bottles or glasses are taken out."

The huge stock of minerals was rapidly disappearing. Ann and Shirley came in and immediately set to work helping Deirdre with the washing-up. "It's even-stevens out there," Shirley said. "Two each, just two more to go."

"They're all mad. That game should be banned,"

Deirdre said.

"Hear, hear!" Ann agreed, as all the women laughed.

"What the hell are we doing here at all?" a woman with a Scottish accent said. "It's us that's mad, to be led and said by those lunatic husbands of ours."

"Ah! well, tonight we'll forgive them," said Shirley. A tremendous roar went up as the last bout ended.

Singing once again commenced, almost as if a choir master was directing operations. All the girls from the hospital and many more came pouring into the bar. "Well matched, three bouts each."

The outcome seemed to please everybody. As the crowd cleared, Tommy, Jimmy and the stewards came in looking exhausted. "Anyone would think it was you fellows were in the ring", Mrs Murphy said. "A nice cup of tea will revive you all. We have the sandwiches all ready for the boxers."

"That's great Nell," Tommy said. "The taxis won't be here till half ten."

Bill Ryan came in looking badly shaken. "What the hell happened you?" Jimmy said.

"I have bad news," Bill said gravely. "I've just been on to St Mary's Hospital. Blackie passed away an hour ago...."

Chapter Seven

DEIRDRE and I sat up late that night. Despite an early start for both of us, the idea of bed and sleep had no appeal. "That same boxing," Deirdre said.

"Can't blame the boxing this time. Jimmy always maintained Blackie was the cleanest fighter he had ever met."

"Makes the way he ended up all the more tragic. I'll ring St. Mary's as soon as I get to work in the morning and find out about the arrangements. Come straight to the hospital after work. No doubt Tommy and Jimmy will be sorting things out during the day."

"We'll have to do something about sorting out our things," I said.

"Bit early for that."

"I mean us getting married," I said. Deirdre laughed. "What's so funny?"

"Funny? I think it's hilarious, you making a proposal of marriage with your legs on the mantelpiece."

"Well, I built it, or at least half of it," I said. "Let's go to bed, I'll propose to you there instead."

"Seriously," she said, "we have a real dilemma. If I announce my engagement, I'll be under instant surveillance at the hospital. If they have the least suspicion, they can put two and two together no bother. That means marriage, end of nursing career. Married women not kept. Don't forget my love, I have another two years to go before I can even sit my final exams."

"Tricky," I agreed. "What's the answer, then?"

"Do you really want to get married?"

"One more remark like that, mate," I said, "and I'm gone. It's not every night I make a proposal of marriage. Let me tell you, there's hundreds of girls out there would jump at a chance like that."

"They'd jump alright," she said. "Off Westminster Bridge. To think I always dreamed of marrying a tall, dark, handsome Prince."

"Not too late yet sweetheart, why don't you get Ranter to introduce you to that Indian Prince? I hear they get their weight in gold every year."

"They'd need that," she said. "How else could they keep a large harem over there, not to mention that little shack in Belgravia."

"When I make my fortune, you can take me home and show me off to all your relations. Don't forget Miss, our crowd owned Munster and built Blarney Castle. I'm really a Prince. We had a sheepdog at home called Prince."

"Hope he's still alive," Deirdre said. "Let's go to bed, you can read me another chapter of 'The Ragged Trousered Philanthropist'. Might bring you back to earth."

A BOUT two dozen people were gathered outside the small chapel at St Mary's Hospital. To our great surprise, the Dublin boxers were standing with Jimmy Palmer and Jack Doyle. Jerry, Frank Coffey and Shirley came to join us.

"The boys decided to stay back." Frank said. "They want to accompany Blackie's remains back to Dublin."

Father Danny arrived from Willesden with Tommy and Mrs Murphy. Moving into the back seat, Deirdre stopped suddenly. Peering over her shoulder, I saw George Logan kneeling at the end of the seat, his head in his hands. A steady stream of familiar faces kept on arriving as the service went on, among them Jock Denver, Snowy and Bill Ryan. Michael Coleman arrived with a group from the job. They stood inside the door, unable to find a seat.

Emerging from the chapel after the service, we found the narrow lane blocked by two taxis. George, Bill Ryan and Jack Doyle entered the first one and moved off without a word to anybody. Father Danny, Mrs Murphy and two other women, moved off in the second.

"We have a private room arranged at the Black Lion," Tommy announced to the crowd assembled outside the church. "Anyone who wants to come along will be welcome."

A lively session was under way when we got there. A melodeon, a fiddle and a tin whistle player in full flight. Jimmy was at the counter as I moved up to get the drinks.

"Why all the big hurry away in the taxis?" I asked.

I felt a tap on the ankle. As the barman moved away, Jimmy said in a whisper, "we're trying to cool George down."

"Over what?" I said.

"My God," he said, his voice even lower, "the

Hazley mob. What they did to poor Blackie.... As
you know," he raised his voice with the return of
the barman, "there's a time and a place for
everything. Everything. *Tuigeann tu?*"

T HE Federation Steward was on his rounds
shortly after starting time next morning.
"General site meeting," he told the shop stewards.

"What's the problem?" I asked Smithy.

"The new site across the road," he said. "They
want to bring in sub-contractors. You know what
that means."

"I'm not too sure."

"Well, you'll be sure after the meeting," he said.

"Brothers," Jimmy Ashcroft commenced. "I feel
sure we have a one hundred per cent turn-out at
this meeting. That means a total of one hundred
and twenty-five. Of that total, sixty-five are
labourers, all union members. The new site is
about to get under way. Yesterday the managing
director of the company invited your works
committee to a meeting. The general foreman and
site foreman were also there. Figures were
produced for materials, labour-costs and market-
value of the houses, to show they cannot remain in
business unless drastic changes are made and sub-
contractors brought in. No need to spell out what
this means.

"To begin with, it means the laying off of most of
you over the next few weeks. Almost immediately,
for fifty per cent of the labourers. It means going
cap-in-hand to a few cut-throat piece-work bosses

who will hire and fire at will. Hire and fire, until they get to a stage where every man is doing work for a lousy twopence or threepence an hour. On your behalf, we have totally rejected the entire package presented by the company. We refute their allegations of low productivity. We refuse to agree to systems which mean a reduction in our working conditions. You can depend on full backing from the Federation. Brothers, I move that this general site meeting unconditionally endorse the stand taken by your site committee."

Jimmy Ashcroft finished his speech to enthusiastic applause. Smithy formally seconded. "Those in favour?" - a sea of hands were raised. "Those against?" - not a single hand.

"Carried unanimously," Jimmy Ashcroft announced as the whistle sounded.

DEIRDRE had our favourite dinner ready, Irish stew. "Got a bit of news for you, honey," I said. "Big meeting today on the site. We could be on strike in a day or two."

"That's all we need," she said. "That letter on the mantelpiece is from Tommy. He has another week's leave. He's going to a friend's house in Brighton for the weekend and coming here on Monday night."

"Good job he wrote anyway," I said. "My nerves have been in bits lately in case he arrived unexpected."

A knock on the door caused me to jump up, dropping my knife on the floor. Deirdre laughed, "it's only Shirley," she assured me. "I asked her to dinner."

Shirley came breezing in. "Wait till I tell ye the news," she said. "Jerry has asked me to marry him."

"I don't believe it," I said, as the two girls burst out laughing.

"Didn't *ask* me," Shirley said, "put it all in a letter." "Ah! poor Jerry," Deirdre said. "Whoever marries him will be a lucky girl."

"I'm still in a state of shock," Shirley said.

"If I'm any judge, Frank Coffey will be in a bigger state of shock," I said, "when he hears the news."

"I think I'll emigrate," Deirdre said.

"Can't see you going anywhere," said Shirley, "you're too much in love. Sometimes I think you pair don't know how lucky you are. It's alright for Jerry to want to get married if he'd make up his mind about where he wants to live. Going back to Ireland is an obsession with him."

"Isn't that what we all want to do?" Deirdre said. "I know somebody," she mocked, "who wants to go back and build a lovely mansion overlooking the Atlantic Ocean."

"Nothing wrong with dreaming," Shirley said. "Jerry's ambition is different. He has a great longing to go back to the farm. Being the eldest, he knows that one day he will own it. If the rest of his brothers and sisters bail out, that could leave me sharing the house with his mother. As far as I'm concerned, living in a house with a mother-in-law would be a fate worse than death."

"You're right there, Shirley," I said, "but who's to say she might want to live with you and Jerry?"

"That's true," Shirley agreed. "Just the same, I wouldn't risk it."

"DON'T leave that bag on the bus," Deirdre warned next morning. "All your clean clothes are in it."

To my great surprise, pickets were already on the entrance to the site, when I arrived.

"A bit sudden," I said.

"No alternative," Smithy replied. "Have a look over the far hedge."

About twenty men were already digging foundations. "Quick work sure enough," I said.

"I'm sorry to tell you that they're all Irish."

"How the hell do you know that?" I asked.

"Jimmy Ashcroft and myself spoke to every one of them before they started."

"Smithy," I said, testily, "you're getting on my wick, to use your favourite expression. They might just as well be English or Chinese."

"You miss the point," Smithy cut me short. "I'm telling you they're Irish because I'm shocked. In twenty five years I have never seen an Irishman pass a picket. We've decided to hold a meeting with them as soon as possible. What you doin' with the bag?" he continued, looking at the hold-all I was carrying.

"Evicted again," I lied. "Landlady needs my bed for a week."

"My missus might, just might, put you up for a week," he said. "She's half Irish, you know. Last Irishman I brought home stayed two years. Couldn't get a word in edge ways between the two of them."

"Smithy, I swear I won't open my mouth, except of course to cope with plenty of bacon, cabbage and spuds at night and a panful of eggs, rashers and sausages in the morning!"

"Blimey, you'll be lucky. You wouldn't get a stodge-up like that Christmas Day in our 'ouse. Oh! by the way, the stewards are making a picket roster in there," he continued, "check what time you're on."

"And me thinking I had a great excuse to have the day off," I said.

ABOUT a dozen fires were lighting all around the open space. A gang surrounded each, waiting for their cans to boil. A small piece of timber or a matchstick with the head removed floated in every can; a sure way of keeping the smoke from ruining the tea.

I moved to where Peter Loftus sat, already well down the can we shared. Peter was considered the greatest hodsman in all London. Well over six feet, he was the only man known to take three rungs of the ladder at a time on the way up, and, like all good hodsman, he only hit two rungs coming down from the top. By an odd coincidence his nearest rival was his best mate, Geordie Moffatt.

I had already heard the story of their famous

competition. Geordie and Peter had worked around the huge field-ranging areas of Greenfield, Kingsbury and South Harrow for about four years, but never for the same builder. Stories about them around the pubs and the dance halls, abounded. Peter's boss, Big Dan Sullivan, and Geordie's boss, Jim Cummins, both from the West of Ireland, were eventually provoked into a heavy bet, to put an end to all arguments.

Sullivan had two pairs of houses ready for top lift. Four hundred and eighty bricks were placed exactly six feet from the bottom of each ladder. The competition was set for one o' clock on a Saturday. The news spread like wildfire to sites up to five miles away, in all directions. They say a thousand men, at least, gathered to see this great feat of skill and fitness. Impromptu bookmakers sprang up everywhere around the field. Pounds and fivers were going down in the fever of excitement that preceded the great fray.

The rules were decided. The bricks had to be stacked four hods high, forty-eight to each stack.

To an earsplitting cheer, the whistle blew and both men started for the scaffold. Excitement grew, as each time they hit the ground not a split second apart. Shouts went up everywhere as onlookers placed more bets. Both men stripped to the waist, intense concentration showing on their faces. As they reached the ladders to descend for the last time, Loftus, making contact with only one rung of the ladder, hit the ground a split second in front of Moffatt. Loftus was declared champion.

Soon afterwards they teamed up and were able to pick their jobs at will and became inseparable mates. Geordie soon became a really popular man in the Irish dance halls, taking readily to reels and sets, and giving a regular exhibition of clog dancing.

Peter, however, could never be drawn on the famous event. "Only one thing to tell you," he'd say: "Geordie got his own back. I introduced him to a smashing girl from Cork and he married her. I had my eye on her, but I was too slow."

Once again the fires were rekindled. There was an abundance of firewood from the rooted up hedges and trees. At least a dozen card schools were in progress: Brag, Pontoon, as well as the old faithful 'twenty-fives'.

A carpenter's apprentice accidentally knocked over his own and another can. The job bully, Gorman, whose can was spilt, viciously attacked the apprentice, knocking him to the ground. The young fellow's father tackled Gorman, only to be sent sprawling, and narrowly escaped ending up across the roaring fire and the boiling tea cans.

"You wouldn't hit your match, Gorman," a man shouted.

"Wouldn't I?" yelled Gorman. "You want a bet?" He threw a fiver on the ground.

"Anyone here got a fiver to lend?" the man beside me said in a voice for all to hear. One of the bricklayers walked forward and threw a fiver beside Gorman's. "Mickey Flynn, the pleasure is all mine."

Mickey Flynn jumped to his feet. Like magic there was a sudden deadly silence. Men moved from all around the clearing, forming a circle around Flynn and Gorman. The soft-spoken man I had been sitting beside had suddenly changed, now he had the look of a killer. In a split second he had planted a left hook smack on Gorman's chin. Gorman's head jerked back. A right to the solar plexus, another straight left to the chin and a right uppercut sent Gorman sprawling on his back with no further interest in the fight, or his surroundings. Flynn walked over and picked up the two fivers. He crumpled one and flicked it to his friend. He moved towards Gorman and pushed the other one straight into his open mouth. He motioned to his friend.

"Get a bucket of water, Charlie," he said. Charlie went to the barrel beside the nearby shed, filled the bucket and lashed it into Gorman's face, then came and sat beside Flynn and myself. "Blimey, you must 'ave plenty, giving that geyser back his fiver."

"Forget it, Charlie," Flynn said. "I'm not that hard up."

Slowly Gorman shook himself awake, rose to his feet and shakily started walking towards the timekeeper's office to collect his cards.

"**D**ID you know Blackie well?" I asked Mickey Flynn, handing him a fresh mug of tea.

"As well as any man could know another man," he replied. "We were members of the one club."

"I know George Logan too," I said boastfully. "And his sister Colette. Jimmy Palmer is a great friend of mine. You know, I'd really love to be a boxer...."

"Would you now?" Mickey said.

"I intend having a go at it, as soon as I build my niche and finish with the Tech. At present I haven't time for anything. It would be great to be able to stand up to a bully, like you just did now."

"Gobshites like him never learn," Mickey said, lighting a cigarette. "A few pints next Saturday night and he's off again. It's the likes of him that gives the rest of us a bad name. If I had my way, I'd deport all the hard-chaws back to Ireland. They should be kept in a cage and only brought out to work in the bog." We both laughed.

"Would you like to do it all over again?" I asked.

"I don't know, I never thought much about it. Ten years ago, when I came to this town, there wasn't much choice. For every one straight boxing manager, there was a dozen crooked ones. Those boys would use you, abuse you, and think nothing of snuffing you out if you didn't do things their way. Ask your friend Jimmy," he said. "If Jimmy Palmer had had good management, he would definitely have gone a long way."

"Was Blackie good?" I asked.

"Too good," Mickey said. "That's why he's dead."

"It's terrible how people get away with the likes of that."

"Get away with what?" Mickey said. "God help your foolish little head...."

"Okay boys," Smithy interrupted, "your turn on the picket. We're expecting three loads of bricks this afternoon."

I walked out over to the picket line, wondering what Mickey meant. Jimmy Ashcroft arrived with the Federation organiser, Dave Elms. The pickets gathered round them. "We're calling a site meeting here at five o'clock and inviting the lads across the road to attend," said Jimmy. "Meantime make sure nothing gets through that gap."

A lorry load of bricks, followed closely by two more, came noisily up the road. The front lorry careered through the gap without changing speed. Miraculously everybody jumped clear, badly shaken by the reckless behaviour of the lunatic behind the wheel. Before anyone could recover, the second and third followed. They stopped short of the clearing, two men and the driver jumping from each cab. Each held a stout iron bar. They moved to the first lorry and, laying the iron bars on the ground at their feet, began to unload.

Ashcroft and Smithy stepped out from the front of the crowd. As soon as Ashcroft began to speak, a shower of bricks came flying towards them. Only by retreating rapidly backwards was it possible for them to avoid being killed.

"We're in a very tricky position here." Mickey Flynn said.

Eight of us were standing at the gap completely isolated. A large group of police jumped from black marias and came quickly towards us.

"You are all breaking the law. Consider

yourselves under arrest."

"We've broken no law," Mickey Flynn replied.

"You can explain that to the Judge," the sergeant continued brusquely.

A sudden impulse made me dash away. As if anticipating my intention, the sergeant sprang to grab me. After half a dozen paces he realised he wouldn't catch me and made a flying tackle. I could feel his fingers touch my heels. A second policeman took up the chase. A gap was opened in the crowd and quickly closed. I was safe in the clearing.

Piles of bricks had been brought from the site and piled all over the place. A great roar split the air, as dozens of policemen with batons drawn, joined by the scabs, came thundering towards the crowd. A concentrated shower of bricks made them just as quickly retreat. Within seconds the lorries were completely wrecked. The bonnets were prised open and bundles of lighted paper thrown in. The speed with which the lorries caught fire was truly frightening. Those nearest made a hasty retreat, throwing themselves on the ground face down, as three sharp explosions occurred almost simultaneously. The flames from the lorries were now reaching high in the air and cutting the road off completely.

For more than half an hour, while the lorries blazed, there was stalemate. Then a police Inspector, appearing for the first time, shouted over a megaphone.

"This is a riot. The penalty for anyone refusing

to surrender is a long term of imprisonment with hard labour. Throw down your weapons and come forward, not more than five at a time."

"You have your shite," a voice rang out from somewhere in the crowd. In spite of all the tension, a general outburst of laughing and cheering followed.

Jimmy Ashcroft emerged from the crowd and started walking towards the police. Holding his hand aloft, to signal clearly for everyone to stay put, he walked beyond the now smouldering lorries, and stopped.

"On behalf of those assembled behind me," he spoke in a loud clear voice, "I want to ask the Inspector one question. Are those nine scabs, wielding iron bars, members of the police force?"

There was complete silence, then the Inspector raised the megaphone to his mouth. "I repeat. This is a riot. These men are standing with the police for their own protection."

Ashcroft again raised his hand. "These scabs arrived on this job armed with iron bars. Nobody attacked them, nobody laid a hand on them, or the police. Remove those scabs, remove the police and every man here will quietly and peacefully disperse."

The Inspector made no reply. Ashcroft slowly walked back and stood at the front of the crowd.

"We must get a phone call through to Harry Adams," Ashcroft told Mickey Flynn. Adams was President of the Bricklayer's Union. "How to get out is the problem. It means crossing the rugby ground and getting over that wall. That means two volunteers, one to hoist up the other."

"Give me the phone number," I said eagerly. "I'll get one of my mates Jerry or Frank."

"There's the office number and the house number," Ashcroft said. "Tell him to get here as soon as possible. Tell him the police have declared our strike to be a riot."

Frank and Jerry both insisted on being part of the mission. The sprint around the sidelines and over the wall went without mishap. Approaching the shops and post office, just ten minutes walk away, my heart missed several beats. Two black marias were parked right in front of the post office, two policemen in each cab. To my profound relief they remained there as I walked across the road and entered the post office.

"Yes, brother Adams is in his office," the man's voice said. When I relayed my message, Harry Adams was brief and to the point. "Tell Jimmy Ashcroft I will be there in an hour or so," he said.

Reaching the front gate of the rugby ground, I gripped the heavy padlock, scrambled to the top and threw myself over. I crossed the grounds and made for the far wall. Frank and Jerry were waiting on the other side and the rope came sailing over in answer to my whistle. I was back safely.

"Harry Adams is a sound man," Ashcroft was assuring the stewards, as I arrived with three cans of tea. They had adjourned to the rear of the crowd to review the situation pending his arrival. The President of the Bricklayer's Union was the recognised T.U.C. spokesman on matters affecting the building industry, and was trusted by the rank and file. "He's the only man," Ashcroft went on, "who can do something about this mess."

A sudden commotion among the crowd, close to where we sat, caused everyone to jump to their feet. Four men had scaled the wall and were demanding to see the shop steward.

"Let the men come forward," Ashcroft immediately took the matter in hand. "Let's hear what they have to say."

"We come from a meeting of the men across the road," the big man said in a Belfast accent. "It looks to us that we have been landed in a dirty situation. I am the ganger, but neither me nor any mawn over yonder want to be responsible for scabbing. We were recruited in Belfast two weeks ago, offered overtime and extra money and our fares paid over, but ne'er a word about what they were letting us in for. We have nothing to go home to, otherwise we would demand our return fares. It was unanimously decided at our meeting to give in our notice."

"That is good news," Ashcroft said, as he shook hands with the ganger and his three companions. Jumping on the nearby scaffold, he raised his hand in his characteristic fashion. "Brothers, the men on the new site, whom we thought to be scabs, were in fact victims of a huge con trick. At great loss and hardship to themselves, they have unanimously decided to throw their lot in with us."

A great cheer followed, as the ganger climbed on

the scaffold and shook hands with Ashcroft. As if by a pre-arranged signal, the men from the new site came surging across the road and over the wall. In the excitement, nobody, not even Ashcroft, noticed the lone figure of Harry Adams, picking his steps past the burned-out lorries.

Ashcroft lost no time ushering Adams, the stewards and the four Belfast men into the dining hall. "If there's any tea left," he said as he passed me, "show how good a socialist you are!"

"You'll get no dinner tonight," Smithy emphasised, "if you fail in that mission."

The four cans were almost boiled when huge rain-drops began to spatter the fire. They were only a forewarning for what was to follow. The heavens overflowed. Within seconds the rain came pouring down, soaking everybody and everything, almost before we realised what was happening. We made a mad rush to the unfinished houses, anywhere to get shelter. By the time I'd found a room that wasn't already packed, I might just as well not have bothered. Soaked to the skin, I felt like stripping off and running out to show my defiance of the elements. My three fellow refugees were from the gang we had looked upon as vermin so shortly before.

The rain stopped just as suddenly as it had begun, only to be followed by lightning - flashes the likes of which I had never seen before. Then another deluge. Listening to the thunder that followed was like being trapped between opposing artillery regiments, opening up the big guns at very close range.

"Mawn, that's a tidy one," one of my new companions said, as the noise abated temporarily. "Wouldn't you think ould nick himself had got hold of the lambegs."

"Sure to God," one of his mates agreed. "Maybe Our Friend up there takes a dim view of the strike!"

"You could be bang-on there, Billy," one of the others went on. "What matter if the boys in blue had to scatter as well." This was my first experience of the Belfast accent.

After a short discussion with the works committee, Ashcroft once again addressed the men. "Harry Adams," he declared, "has arranged a meeting with the management in their head office. The police have agreed to withdraw in the meantime. We'll report back shortly."

While we were waiting to hear the result of the discussions, Jerry went out to buy an evening paper. It was full of the day's events. 'RIOT AT TWICKENHAM BUILDING SITE. THREE LORRIES BURNED OUTRIGHT...' 'Our correspondent reports that the trouble began at Twickenham, through friction between two rival Irish gangs.'

"Oh, the fairy tales of England!" was Jerry's comment.

T HE general feeling was that a long dispute was inevitable. The serious confrontation with the police; the wrecking of three lorries; the clear warning from the Inspector that the iniquitous Trades Dispute Act would be invoked; everything pointed to protracted negotiations with slim hope of an early solution. The atmosphere was tense as the delegation arrived back and mounted the platform.

"Brothers," Ashcroft commenced. "The present phase of our discussions with management have just concluded. The Managing Director of the company considered the matter of this dispute so serious that he interrupted his holidays in France. Progress has been made in so far as the implementation of the Riot Act is concerned. This order, I am pleased to report, has been withdrawn by the police." Loud cheers greeted this announcement. "Work will resume tomorrow morning pending further discussions. Work on the new site will stop, pending further discussions. The situation of the Belfast workers will be given top priority at tomorrow's meeting with management." This announcement was greeted with prolonged applause and cheering. "The police have agreed to keep all charges regarding damage etc. until a meeting with your shop stewards, fixed for Monday morning."

Widespread consternation was obvious at this seemingly too easy and satisfactory end to all the tension and drama. "How the hell did ye get things sorted out so handy?" I asked Smithy as we sat in the bus.

"Wheels within wheels, maite. That's how. Our Managing Director is a Conservative candidate in the forthcoming general election. His brother-in-law is the present Home Secretary. You couldn't give the opposition a stick like that at such a critical time, now could you?"

"Sounds crazy," I said.

"Crazy it is, maite," Smithy agreed. "Didn't you know democracy is a crazy system? Sometimes it works if you know how to use it. Harry Adams is the boy for that."

"Oh! Never mind democracy," I cried, my sudden change of tune startling him.

"Gor Blimey," he said, "what's come over you then?"

"My bag," I said, "every stitch I had is in it!"

Smithy was still laughing as we reached the house.

Chapter Eight

MY date with Deirdre outside the hospital was just as exciting as my very first with her. Our highly publicised strike had caused great speculation when she, Tommy and Gladys had called to see the Murphys. Suddenly she saw my new fifty shilling suit.

"It's lovely," she said, "but why did you buy a suit so soon again?"

"Couldn't resist a bargain," I lied. I couldn't wait to tell Deirdre the good news about the strike being settled.

"I have great news too," she said. "I'm getting a week's holiday and then going to the Children's Hospital. I can't wait to get working with the kids."

"A glutton for punishment, sweetheart," I said.

"You should know," she retorted. "Shirley has got herself a new job as well. Tourist Guide at the Savoy Hotel. Wants us to go on her maiden trip next week. Should be great crack. One bit of news I was warned to keep secret. Tommy and Gladys are getting engaged at Christmas."

"Hope it's before I go home," I said. "Maybe I should tell you another bit of news I intended keeping a secret. My bag was robbed."

"How I ever got mixed up with a nit-wit like you," she said, "I just cannot understand."

"There's gratitude, and me riskin' my life for freedom and democracy."

"Let's go to the pictures," she said. "If a shower comes, that suit will be washed away."

MICHAEL Coleman and the other foremen had kept a low profile during the strike. Their jobs were at stake too, and everybody knew that. Michael arrived on the scaffold next morning. "Got a bit of news," he said. "The men from Belfast are all off to the Gold Coast. The company have a contract for a big aerodrome out there."

"Wouldn't mind a trip like that myself," I said.

"Ah! you wouldn't do that," Smithy said. "We'd never finish this job without you."

"If I get the turkey out of this job, whoever likes can finish it. I'll be out with the Wren Boys Stephen's Day, Smithy."

"'ope it keeps fine for you," Smithy said, "whatever it is. Maybe you'll send me a card to Wormwood Scrubs. Ashcroft says all the stewards are being done for incitement and God knows what. Seems we're all in breach of the 'Trade Disputes Act' after all. Apart altogether from the lorries, we were breaking the law, even calling a strike."

"There's always that job in the Gold Coast," I said.

"Blimey," Smithy replied, "I'd rather take my chances in the Scrubs."

THE front page story in the Sunday papers reminded me of Mickey Flynn's cryptic remark.

'Well known boxing proprietor Ron Hazley, his brothers George and Geoff, also the well known boxing trainer Don Cox, all victims of a vicious attack by unknown gang. All four seriously injured. A hospital spokesman would make no comment, except to say all four men were in intensive care. The attack took place at the well known Thames Side Boxing Club owned by Mr. Ron Hazley. The Club was completely destroyed by fire. A police spokesman said the fire was deliberately started by the gang. No arrests have been made....'

In the days that followed, rumours filled in the details of the story. Four masked men - some said five - had entered the Boxing Club after the last of the young boxers had left for Punchy Armstrong's pub. They had beaten the four boxing bosses unconscious and dragged them out to the laneway before setting fire to the club. If anyone suspected who the masked men were, they were saying nothing.

Deirdre was back on night work so I went to Willesden alone. "Oh!" Mrs Murphy greeted me, "your suit is lovely."

"Don't you start," I said as she ushered me into the living room. To my surprise, Deirdre's brother, his girlfriend Gladys, Jerry Fitzsimons and Shirley were sitting down to tea. "Look at what the cat brought in," Mrs Murphy announced. "We've been hearing of your great exploits in Twickenham."

"A thing of nothing," I said, to quote my Da. "After all somebody had to risk life and limb. What matter if I lost all my worldly goods, it was all in a good cause."

"You should claim the Union for the price of that

suit," Jerry said, with a glint in his eye.

"I think it's smashin'," Shirley said.

"I'd love a suit of that material. I might get one like that for going home," Jerry kept on.

"Listen Jerry," I said, "if you say another word about this suit, you'll never *see* home."

"Hear, hear," Mrs Murphy said as she returned from the scullery with a rasher, egg and two sausages. "Any more slagging about that suit and nobody gets apple tart."

Looking at the clock on the mantelpiece I spotted a large photograph. "That's new," I said. I gazed at the unmistakable features of Blackie and Jimmy Palmer. Dressed in their boxing gear, Blackie was landing a mock left hook to Jimmy's chin.

"By the way," Mrs Murphy said, "did you know Ron Hazley is dead. 'twill be all over the papers tomorrow."

"T HAT was the longest week of my entire life," I told Deirdre as we lay on the heavy blanket before the glowing fire."It's nice to be home."

"It was like that with me too. It's just as well I was working nights," Deirdre said.

"I missed the fireplace. With all Smithy's knowledge, he hasn't a fireplace like that."

"You know what?" Deirdre said, "it didn't look the same with our photograph missing."

"Couldn't we announce our engagement the same day as Tommy and Gladys?" I said.

"That would be out of the question.It would spoil

their big day altogether."

"How thoughtful of you," I said testily.

"We'll have our big night, don't you worry, my love," Deirdre soothed. "Poor Tommy, think of all the lonely nights he has at present, and Gladys as well."

"Okay darling, you win."

"Just give me a big hug and a kiss. Tell me a story and let's forget about that stupid world out there."

"My Da told me a story once and he swore it was true. This very rich family lived in a mansion on the banks of the Smearla river. They had great tracts of land. A thousand acres or more. Hundreds of cattle, many horses and thousands of sheep. They had many servants and a large family. Donal, their eldest son, was twenty one. He was tall and handsome and full of the joy of living. He loved Irish music and Irish dancing, unlike his parents, who lived very quietly and had few local friends.

"Donal fell madly in love with the ploughman's daughter Eileen. She was seventeen and beautiful, beyond compare. When Donal told his parents he wanted to marry her, they lost their reason completely. They gave him an ultimatum to give up seeing her for ever, or leave the house and be totally dispossessed. For weeks he suffered his ordeal in silence. All his pleading fell on deaf ears. Finally he had to break the news to Eileen. He had enough money to pay his fare to America. Once there, he would earn enough money to send her the fare and they would live happily ever after. Long into the night they kissed and cried, gripped in each others arms, hoping the dawn would never come. Alas, the dawn came only too soon. They kissed and embraced once more under their very own willow tree.

"Eileen stood a long time after Donal disappeared from sight on the narrow winding road. Only by a superhuman effort did she suppress the terrible urge to follow him. Throwing herself on the ground, now lonely and desolate, she cried for a long time. The ship ran into a fierce storm and was sunk with not one survivor. My Da used to sing a song about them which he claimed was written by his uncle."

"Oh! do sing it for me," Deirdre pleaded. "That's a terrible sad story...."

> It was on a bright morning in Summer
> as the sky larks sang loudly on high
> and the sun it shone down most melodious
> on all that reigns under the sky.
> When along by the woodlands I wandered
> and down by the slopes I did slide
> It was there I beheld a fair damsel
> on the banks of the sweet Smearla side.
>
> My eyes they grew dim in a moment
> as towards this fair maid I did go
> saying tell me the cause of your sorrow
> I am anxiously longing to know.
> She said I once courted a young man
> but the ocean it now us divides

and it leaves me to wander in sorrow
by the banks of the sweet Smearla side.

What trade did your true lover follow
or what name did your true love go by.
His name it was Donal Fitzgerald
and indeed I will tell you no lie.
His parents they own a large mansion
wherein a young prince might reside
It's just at the foot of the mountain
on the banks of the sweet Smearla side.

That some fairy gale may enchant him
and roll him back over the tide.
Back home again to his Eileen
on the banks of the sweet Smearla side.

"That was beautiful," Deirdre said, "and so sad."

"Wipe away your tears, you romantic ould fool," I chided, "and let's go to bed. No danger of me ever going off like that," I said, as we embraced.

"No danger of anyone stopping you," she said with characteristic devilment.

"**A**LL the shop stewards are summoned," Mickey Flynn said, as we waited for the whistle to go next morning. "They've done us under the Trades Disputes Act. Could cause an awful lot of trouble."

"I don't care if they hang you," I said, "so long as they wait till after Christmas. I'd hate that trip to be shagged up."

"Another bit of news," he went on. "Hazley is being cremated on Saturday."

"Oh!" I said, "so what?"

"Well, I'm going along to represent the club."

"Surprise, surprise, I didn't think you cared."

"Think again, mate," he said. "Don't you know we all care. All the clubs will be represented. I saw Jimmy Palmer last night. He will be there representing the Vale."

"I swear to God, Mickaleen, you're a rum crowd."

"A holy terror mate," he said, "a holy terror."

"Mind if I come along with you," I asked, "seeing as it's Saturday. I've never been to a cremation."

"You're welcome," Mickey said, "if you like that sort of thing."

Like that sort of thing is right. I thought of Mickey's words as I sat close to the front and wishing I had never come. The crematorium was packed, making it quite impossible to slip out. What I hadn't expected was the sight of the symbolic methylated spirit flames licking around the coffin. The Clergyman mounted the rostrum and spoke in grave tones about violence, the grieving family and the hereafter. I closed my eyes to shut out the flames. What purpose did this service have, I kept asking myself. Up to now I had felt that cremation was a better way. It spared relatives the trauma of seeing a loved one lowered into a grave and hearing the sound of clay thumping off the coffin. Looking at those flames, I began to wonder was there much to choose.

It was good to get out into the bright sunshine.

People stood around in groups, many shaking hands and greeting old friends. Jimmy was talking with Jack Doyle and his woman friend. Jack was resplendent in a pinstripe suit, his woman friend in a mink coat. I learned from Mickey who all the other famous boxers were; Eric Boone, Mel Tarelton, Len Harvey, Jack Peterson, Jock McEvoy, Joe Beckett and Peter Kane. All household names.

"I'll introduce you to the daddy of them all," Mickey said, walking towards a little man surrounded by a cheerful crowd, listening to his every word. "Meet the king," Mickey said as I pushed my way in to shake hands with Billy Wilde.

"A very big crowd," I said to Jimmy afterwards, as we sat on the bus on our way to the Spotted Dog. "Yeah," he replied, a strange glint in his eye, "a very big crowd. I'd say about half of them from the murder squad."

THAT'S coming on nicely," Tommy Murphy said, as he threw his experienced eye over my niche. For three weeks now, two nights each week, all my concentration was centred on this project. I was only too well aware of the honour. Tommy picked a protege to tackle this task only if he was reasonably sure he was ready.

"Tell me, Tommy," I asked, "why the reinforced concrete base?" The base which he had himself cast was set on a temporary dry brick base, about three feet above the ground. From the start, I had wondered why the base had been accurately shaped with a highly trowelled finish.

"If I tell you," he said, "will you promise you won't let it go to your head."

"For crying out loud, mate, cross my weary heart. Now you've made me doubly curious."

"I'll tell you," he said. "Father Danny wants a niche in the flower garden outside the church."

"Holy God," I cried, as I slumped down, knocking over the small stack of bricks. Both of us broke into laughter.

"Some sculptor has presented the church with a statue of Blessed Martin," Tommy went on.

"I'm glad this work of art is nearly finished," I said. "That bit of news has knocked me into a cocked hat. I think I'll go home, put on my latest new suit and take Deirdre to the West End."

"Sight seeing again," Tommy said, shaking his head, "poor Deirdre."

"Envy is one of the deadly sins," I said. "If you want to know, we have a table booked at Quaglinos. Apparently the Prince of Wales has a party booked in as well."

"Better get that mortar out from under your nails, " he shouted after me, as I bade him the soldiers farewell.

"Good job you're early, " Deirdre said as I came in. Shirley was busy doing something with her hair. "Jerry is calling any time now and we're going to the West End to see a picture."

"Gor Bloimey," I said, in my best cockney, "you must be clairvoyant. I've just been codding Tommy about us going to the West End."

"Well, we're not codding," Deidre said. "Shirley

has four complimentary tickets to see 'Twenty Years a-Growing'."

Shirleys new job was a God-send; she got passes for all the West End shows.

"IT'S all hands on deck Saturday afternoon," Tommy said after the Union meeting Monday night. "Bill Ryan is bringing the lorry around to move the niche. The unveiling will take place after twelve o'clock Mass on Sunday. Frank Coffey and Jerry Fitzsimons are working at the brick column. You'd better start praying to Blessed Martin for fine weather."

"I'll pray alright," I said,"that the niche doesn't fall asunder. "

Like everything he put his hand to, Tommy had thought well in advance about the mechanics of this operation. The two holes he had left below the base were just big enough to slide in the two steel joists Bill Ryan had brought along. Practically the entire bricklayers' committee plus Peter, John, Frank, Jerry and myself allowed three men at the ends of the joists, with Tommy hovering, as vigilant as a well-trained sheep dog. The journey to the church was slow, the unloading careful. After much cautious manoeuvring, Tommy expressed his satisfaction with a clear 'that's her'.

"Tell ye what," Father Danny spoke for the first time since the operation began. "Let's all go to the Spotted Dog. I'll buy the first round,"

"Now I'm getting to like you," Bill Ryan said, patting Father Danny on the shoulder as we all piled on the back of the lorry.

"Not a bad night's work for a gang of heathens," Jimmy remarked loudly.

"Heathens or no heathens," Jerry said, "Blessed Martin has performed his first miracle."

"How come, Jerry?" I asked.

"Didn't Father Danny say he was buying a round?"

"He did say that," Father Danny cut in, "and I repeat, the *first* one."

"Bless my soul," Jimmy said. This caused the biggest laugh.

"Will you look what's behind us," Frank said.

Sure enough, there was a black maria in no great hurry to pass us out.

Alighting from the lorry at the Spotted Dog, Jimmy was confronted by two plain clothes men.

"We want you down at the station to answer a few questions," one of them said. "We'll travel in the car," the other one said, indicating the unmarked black car across the street.

"I'd like to go along," Father Danny said.

"That won't be necessary," the first one said decisively.

Jimmy moved across the road. The black car moved away speedily, the black maria following close behind. At Father Danny's request, the barman rushed upstairs to ring a taxi. When it arrived, Father Danny and Tommy left immediately, as the rest of us sat down in silence to have our drink.

Bill Ryan quickly finished his pint and offered

Jerry, Frank and myself a lift around to Murphy's. Mrs Murphy already had the news from a member of the Committee. No words were spoken as she handed us a cup of tea. Finally Bill Ryan broke the silence.

"The niche looks great, Nell. Everything went like a dream. Never saw Tommy worry so much about any operation. He was to go around later to help Father Danny with the statue."

To our great relief, Father Danny and Tommy arrived, followed by Jimmy and another man.

"Thought you were rid of me, Nell," Jimmy said cheerfully. "This is Fred Abraham, he's a solicitor."

"Another five minutes and I was gone for the night," Fred said. "It's our tenth wedding anniversary. New rig-out, the lot. If I don't get home quickly it could be my last."

"Thanks for the lift," Tommy said.

"Tell me before you go," Mrs Murphy said. "Is everything alright?"

"I think so," Fred said reassuringly. "They wanted to know Jimmy's movements on the night the Thames Side Club was attacked. Father Danny was able to assure them he spent the whole night here with him, Tommy and yourself."

"Indeed he did, I remember the night well."

"Wish me luck," Fred said, rising to go. "Your troubles are over, mine are about to begin."

"With all them shenanigans, I missed my little drink", Father Danny said mournfully.

"You missed getting that round as well", Bill Ryan said. "Blessed Martin came to your aid there alright."

"Hould your whisht, Bill Ryan," Mrs Murphy scolded arriving from the scullery with a large bottle and a tray of glasses.

"More power to your elbow Nell," Bill said. "Is it really the holy water?"

"Best you can get," she replied. "All the way from Belmullet."

"My ould fella has been making poteen for fifty years," Tommy said, "never caught once. Mind you the fact that the superintendent is a first cousin of Nell's has helped greatly over the last ten years!"

Before our glasses were filled, the door opened and Dan Lunn walked in followed by George Logan. George was immaculately dressed in the clothes of a priest, the heavy muscles of his neck bulging over the snow-white collar.

"That's torn the arse out of it now altogether," Bill Ryan said as the laughing died down.

"Mind your language, Bill Ryan," Mrs Murphy admonished, as renewed laughter broke out.

Obviously George was still a prime target for the police. Ann and Shirley arrived to accompany Deirdre and myself to the unveiling. "Just typical", Shirley groaned, "bloody English weather."

"The day is young, girls," I consoled them.

THE church was more crowded than usual. The sermon was dispensed with, and after only a few announcements the Monsignor, followed by Father Danny and the altar boys, moved slowly down the middle aisle. Outside a huge umbrella was held over him, another for Father Danny. Umbrellas sprouted everywhere as the heavy rain came splashing down. The Monsignor said a few words which only those close to him could catch. Then he pulled away the blue silk sheet. Poor Blessed Martin looked doleful.

"What a shame," Shirley said.

"The niche is beautiful," Deirdre whispered, squeezing my arm.

"Looks great in the rain," I said.

"You'd think the bricks were french-polished."

"Let's go", I said, "Father Danny has agreed to make good his promise in the Spotted Dog, just as soon as he gets rid of the head man."

Chapter Nine

THE next day it was still raining. Michael Coleman asked Jerry and myself into his office. "Saw Dan Lunn and Tommy last night," he said. "They have a job down in Bedfordshire and they want both of you down there for a week or so. A new boilerhouse. Are we on?"

"Dare we say no?" Jerry said.

"Wouldn't advise it," Michael said, laughing. "Should be a bit of crack anyway. Dan is bringing George down as well."

I grabbed Jerry as he threw his arms in the air and almost tumbled through the open door of Michael's office.

"Matter of fact," Michael said, after we recovered from the shock. "It's not 'George' that's going with ye, it's 'Patrick Murphy'. *Tuigeann tu?*"

"What happened 'Father' Murphy?" I asked.

"Oh! he resigned," Michael said. "He didn't like taking orders from the Cardinal!"

"One thing, Michael," I said, "what about our contribution to the going home fund?"

"I'll look after that," Michael assured us. "Half the country is down with the flu. No problem."

We took the train to Bedford. "We'll be met at the station," said Dan. "Have you ever driven in a Rolls Royce?" he asked George.

"No", George said. "I'll try anything once, except a black maria."

The car that waited for us at the bus stop wasn't a Rolls Royce, but a huge Ford Saloon. The young lady who drove it was stunningly beautiful, with a charming smile. She shook hands and ushered us into the car. Dan sat with her in the front. Fifteen minutes later we were driving up a tree-lined avenue to the biggest house I had ever seen. The black car swept around the avenue to the left, coming to a halt outside a huge iron gate. Our driver sounded the horn.

"All yours, Dad," she said, as the tall man in tweeds opened the gate.

"We'll go to the library. My son will go over the plans with you, Mr Lunn. No doubt a cup of tea would go down well after your journey. "My son Geoffrey," the tall man in tweeds said, as he introduced the young man who rose to greet us. "Geoffrey did these plans as a project for his final year."

Dan went to the huge table where the plans were laid out. A young maid arrived with a big pot of tea and hot buttered scones.

"This is the life," George whispered. "I wonder how far is it to the nearest pub?"

"We've decided to go into pigs," the boss said, as he joined us. "I was in Mayo last year and saw some of Mr Lunn's work. I understand you boys are going to build the new boiler house."

"That's right," Jerry said. "Never thought I'd see the day we'd be installing central heating for pigs." "Makes you think, right enough," George said. "Next thing they'll be giving them is bathrooms."

"Matter of fact," the boss said, as the laughter died down, "Geoffrey has a bathroom in the plan. Not for the pigs, of course, it's for anybody working with them. We're also installing a foot bath. Our new vet is stone mad on hygiene. I suppose if you're planning to deal with a thousand of the blighters at a time, it's as well to be careful."

"A thousand?" I gasped.

The boss laughed. "The way things are shaping up at present," he said, "this country will need all the food we can produce. I had three years as a submarine commander during the last lot. We've fallen so far behind the Germans, I shudder to think of a new war."

"I got away lightly," he continued, raising his left hand to reveal a shiny leather glove with the fist in a permanent clench. The glove reached well above the end of his tweed sleeve.

The maid arrived to announce a lorry load of bricks had arrived. We followed her out to the courtyard. The foundations were already laid for the boiler house and the huge boiler already assembled on its base. The lorryman was delighted with three unexpected helpers. Dan and Geoffrey appeared as the unloading was completed. "The cement and mortar will be delivered this afternoon," Dan announced. "We start work in the morning, eight o'clock."

George moved to where the lorryman and I were standing. "Do you pass any pub?" he asked him.

"Drop you in the village," the lorryman said. "It's about five miles."

"Okay Dan," George said. "We'll just go for a couple of pints and walk back. 'twill give us an appetite for the dinner."

"I'm coming with ye," Dan said, "just in case ye might lose your way coming back." He winked at Geoffrey, as we climbed aboard.

The lorry stopped at the edge of the village. "We'll walk up," Dan said. "Our friend takes a right here. He won't take a drink."

'Biddenham', the sign said.

"Village is right," Dan Lunn remarked. "It must be the richest village in the world."

Every house was set back from the road, and they all looked as if they were owned by millionaires. As we stood to admire one particularly beautiful three storey mansion, the sudden appearance of two bulldogs cut short our gawking. No sooner had we reached the next gate, but two more dogs greeted us, this time an Alsatian and a sheepdog.

"Let no one talk to them," Dan said. "If they hear an Irish accent they'll go mad altogether."

Across the road more dogs took up the barking. So far not a single human being had appeared.

We stopped to admire the elaborate war memorial. The carved stonework was of a very high quality. Five names were commemorated. "Never know our luck," George said, "maybe there's no men left here at all."

The pub looked as quiet as the rest of the village. "Let me do the talking," Dan said as we reached the door.

"Good day to you," he said to the startled white-haired man standing behind the counter. "Can we have four pints of mild and bitter please. We're down here to do some work for Sir Malcolm." This information had the desired effect. The man visibly relaxed. "Don't often have strangers in," he said. "We get quite busy at night."

"It's a good pint anyway," George remarked. After one mighty gulp the pint glass was empty on the table. "That walking is thirsty work, give us four more of the same," he called to the white-haired man. "Ask him how far it is to the next watering hole," he said to Dan.

"Oh", the man shouted back. "Twenty minutes will bring you in to Bedford."

"We'll ramble in after another pint," Dan said. "I need a new trowel."

The walk to Bedford was a really memorable one. Everybody agreed the scenery, not to mention the greenery, was equal to anything we knew at home. Cattle grazed in luscious meadows. Rabbits gambolling in a small field made us stand and laugh for more than ten minutes. The rabbits scurried away in panic as a fox came slouching along the hedge. Further along the road, a blackbird responding to the June-like sunshine held us spellbound with its beautiful and oh so familiar song. Not one small house had we seen so far. The houses we did pass were at least a quarter of a mile apart, all situated well back from the road and all with an air of wealth and prosperity.

"Have a look," Jerry said, as we gazed at a stately edifice. The niche with a stone eagle set to the left of the huge open stone porch was really eye-catching.

"Only one thing wrong," Jerry said. "It doesn't compare with the brick job."

"Oh! now," Dan corrected, "a brick niche would be completely out of tune with the whole structure. The man that cast that one knew his job too."

"'twould be a foolish garsun that would question your judgment Dan," Jerry said cheerfully, as we moved away.

"Never mind your niche," George said, gazing over a high stone wall.

Pulling myself up and gazing over it, my eyes fell on a huge orchard with apple and pear trees drooping with fruit. Within seconds George had hoisted Jerry and myself over.

"I'll go for the pears," I told Jerry as he set about the Russet tree. "Throw me your hat," I called to Dan, as my pockets were bulging.

The sudden sharp unmistakable bang, then a second bang of a double-barrelled gun, caused Jerry and myself to freeze. The pellets whistled through the pear tree over my head, sending leaves fluttering and some pears crashing to the ground. Jerry sprang for the wall with me close on his heels. We needed no assistance over the wall, falling at the feet of Dan and George who were in convulsions of laughter.

George set off at a sharp pace, the rest of us very close behind. Nobody spoke till we got round a sharp bend on the road, then we all sat down. Jerry and I just sat there until our hearts were back somewhere near their normal position, while

Dan and George continued laughing and munching pears.

Dan bought a Brades twelve-inch trowel. Anyone else would think every trowel in the box was exactly alike. Not so Dan Lunn. With his skilled, experienced hand he weighed each one up in turn. Finally settling on one of them, he handed it to me. "Just feel that," he said.

"It sure is a beauty."

"Got news for you," Dan said. "You need that trowel more than I do, the one you're using is a holy show."

"It's one of Murphy's," I protested.

"It *was* one of Murphy's. "Nell wouldn't use that thing in the garden."

"Okay," I said, "you win. But if I run out of money, you'd better be carrying...."

Dan spent ten more minutes sorting out a trowel for himself.

A few doors from the hardware shop, I halted the boys in front of a jeweller's window. "Since you're so good at picking trowels Dan," I said, "maybe you'd give me a hand in here."

Dan looked puzzled as he, Jerry and George followed me inside. Two girls stood inside the counter. To say they looked a bit worried would be putting it mildly.

"What can we do for you?" one of them said.

"I want to buy an engagement ring," I replied. George spluttered something, causing the other two to laugh. "Don't mind those hobos," I assured the girls. "No romance, no souls. Give me a nice engagement ring."

"What price had you in mind?" she asked. Once again the boys began to laugh. "Anything for about half a crown," Jerry said.

"Listen, love," I said, "what kind of a ring would I get for a fiver?"

"A very nice one," she said, reaching under the glass-topped counter for a tray. "Your fiancee should be here, of course, to try them on, of course, we'll change it if the size is wrong."

"Okay" I said, "try one of these on yourself. Let's see your hand. If I'm any judge, you're a ringer."

"Ringer!" she said. "That's good, that is."

The one she recommended was given a one hundred per cent okay by the three hobos. The girl found a beautiful box and expertly parcelled it in blue and gold paper. Before leaving I plucked a huge pear from each of my coat pockets and presented one each to the girls. "From our own orchard," I said.

"Oh, ta," the girls said together. "Hope she likes the ring."

"A bloody fine trick," Jerry said, as we reached the street. "What's Shirley going to think?"

"Shirley will think nothing," I said, "because you will have to get her something very special before we go back." We followed George and Dan into a pub on the corner of the street.

George and Dan got to the counter through the packed bar. "Four pints of mild and bitter," George said to the barman.

The barman looked at an older man who stood a few feet away inside the counter. The older man shook his head slowly.

"Sorry," the barman said, "we can't serve Irishmen."

"We carry English money," George said sharply. I could see his shoulders hunch and his whole body rigid, sure signs of action. The hubbub in the bar stopped as if by magic, a tense atmosphere of anticipation suddenly taking over. Dan stepped closer to George, placing his hand on his arm. "*Patrick*," Dan emphasised the Patrick. "Let's go."

George slowly turned his head, a look of pain in his doleful eyes. For some seconds that felt much longer, the two men stared silently into each others eyes. Then George, with a final look at the older man behind the counter, turned and moved slowly towards the door. I held my breath. God, I thought, let nobody pass any remark now. If so the only miracle I have ever witnessed will surely fail. I held the door open as George, Dan and Jerry moved out to the street.

A man in overalls followed us through the door. "I just want to say one thing. I consider that a lousy trick," the man said. "Every Irish person in this town is being treated like a leper because of a few bad pills. The publicans put a bar on all the Irish lads. Then they wonder why the whole of McAlpine's crew, a couple of hundred of them, cooped up all week in Nissen huts, come into town and cause trouble. The politicians or the trade unions are doing damn all to sort things out."

"Fair enough," Dan said. "We appreciate you coming out. Go back and finish your drink, we're heading back to Biddenham."

"He can stuff his drink," the man said. "I'm away home to get the grub."

R EACHING the edge of the town, I went into a small grocer's shop. An old lady greeted me cheerfully. Yes, she would be glad to make sandwiches from the sliced pan and a pound of ham.

I had to run to catch up with the boys who plodded on in silence.

The sandwiches got a sudden death, but the apples and pears only went part of the way to slake the dreadful thirst. "There she shines," Dan said, as the Biddenham pub came into view. "Just in time to save us from death through dehydration."

The lounge looked a good deal more cheerful, now that it was three quarters full. However, when all eyes are turned on one and conversation ceases, it makes one feel terribly exposed, naked almost. That's how it felt as the four of us made our way to the bar. The white-haired man was now standing serenely surveying the scene, with his back to the shelves. Two younger men were very busy rushing around. The white-haired man came to the counter and greeted us in a friendly way. "You found your way back then," he said. "Geoffrey called down an hour ago to give you a lift. He's in the bar enjoying a game of darts, maybe you'd like to join him there."

"Sounds a very good idea," Dan said.

"This is the best way," the barman said, raising the counter flap and ushering us through to the bar counter. Geoffrey waved from the far end where he stood marking the board.

"I remember your drink," the white-haired man said, as he set up four pints of mild and bitter. A wave from Geoffrey, and Dan's pound was left untouched.

"Some change from that other kip," Jerry said. "I would have gone to war there, only I didn't want to get you guys into trouble."

"I know," Dan said. "I could see you were raring to go."

"Yeah," said Jerry, "raring to go through the door faster than Jessie Owens."

George enjoyed this crack, having now completely simmered down.

Close by at the bar, five or six men were having a hilarious time. A huge man, with a neck like a bull, was doing most of the talking and entertaining.

"Listen Tiny," one of his companions said. "It's your round. 'ave you lost the use of your arm?"

"Thought Geoffrey might 'ave included us in that last round," the big man answered.

"That's no excuse," his pal persisted.

"Ah! get stuffed," the big man said decisively. "Maybe one of the Paddies will stand a round." This remark was made loud enough for us not to miss. Harmless enough, as far as it went. "Clever man the boss. You must 'and it to 'im," the big man went on. "Who would know better about building pig 'ouses than Paddies." This caused a big laugh.

Not again, I thought. George had now cocked his ear and was breathing heavily, staring at his half-finished pint on the counter.

"There's a seat down at the end," Dan said, lifting his pint with a motion to us to move. "Are you right, Patrick?" he said, taking hold of George's arm. George whipped his arm away, drank up his pint and slapped the empty glass back on the counter.

"Four more pints of mild and bitter," he said to the white-haired man, "and send a drink down to Geoffrey."

"Knows how to lick too," the big man said to his companion. "My old man told me straight, 'e was over there 1920 and '21. They live with the pigs over there. 'Struth."

George handed us the pints and collected his change.

"I heard that remark, Tiny," the white-haired man said sternly, "enough of that talk."

"Sorry Guv," Tiny replied. "We was just talkin' about pigs."

He lifted his pint from the counter, raised it to his lips and turned slowly around towards George. Still with the glass to his mouth, he burst out laughing. A mouthful of beer went splashing into the side of George's face and over his neck. George waited till Tiny had replaced his glass on the counter. Then, grabbing him by the collar, he spun him round and put all his fifteen stone behind his right fist. The blow landed straight on Tiny's mouth. He went tumbling backwards, landing ten feet away between two tables. Few men would recover too fast from such a pile driver. All the frustration, all the anger and the hurt bottled up inside a proud, sensitive breast over the last hours were unleashed in that cultivated right hand.

Tiny got to his knees, spitting blood and two or three broken teeth onto the floor. Slowly he raised himself to a crouching position and quickly threw his coat off, flinging it over his shoulder. Now every man in the room was standing. The three small tables on either side were pulled tight against the wall. The clear, masterly voice of Geoffrey rang out from the back of the room. "Let nobody interfere. There is no other way to settle this matter."

"Leave 'im to Tiny," a voice called from near the bar.

George stood waiting, his hands by his sides. Slowly Tiny shuffled cautiously towards him, a murderous look on the huge blood-spattered face. Stabbing out his left hand at George's face, he suddenly brought up a vicious right uppercut, intended for where it would do most damage. This well known trick of the seasoned street fighter did not fool George. With a sudden body swerve, he was on his toes, sending a left and a right in rapid succession to Tiny's right eye and the point of his chin.

It was evident that this lumbering giant had no

hope of getting anywhere on a fisticuffs basis with the best fighting machine known to the pubs, clubs and streets of London.Tiny lunged forward, his hands covering his face, now determined to get George in a clinch. He almost succeeded and as George burst free, crashing his fists to the underside of Tiny's ribs, Tiny's right boot came ripping upwards, only a fraction of an inch from its target. It was a do or die effort that did not succeed, but threw Tiny badly off balance. George took full advantage. A lightning barrage of lefts and rights to the head had Tiny reeling. As he staggered forward, George sidestepped and brought a finishing rabbit punch to bear. Tiny slumped to the floor, face downwards.

Dan Lunn had quietly ordered four large bottles. He picked the bag off the counter and followed George, Jerry and myself through the door.

"Open one of them bottles," George said as we got outside the village. "That's thirsty work." He was relaxed now for the first time since we had made our exit from the pub in Bedford.

A number of dogs started barking as if to bid us farewell. "Fuck the dogs and their owners too," George said. We laughed heartily, as Dan handed Jerry and me our large bottles.

Half a mile up the road, the huge black car caught up with us. "Lost a game of darts over that carry on," Geoffrey quipped.

"Pity about you," Jerry retorted. "How about the drinks we missed. 'A nice quiet week in the country will do ye the world of good'." Jerry loved to mimic Dan.

"Well we're making a good start," I said.

"Yeah," Jerry cut me short. "That nice man with the shotgun was a howl."

"I've got news for you," Geoffrey said. "That nice man was indeed a nice woman. Mrs Rogers is always on the alert. She thought it was a gang of young fellows. They have her damned. Her husband is in hospital at present. He lost a leg same time as the boss got his lot. Gives him a lot of trouble."

"You know them well so," Dan said.

"Well," Geoffrey laughed. "Since she was my nanny, I ought to. They manage that place for my brother. He's in the navy at present. It's in the blood I suppose ever since Drake. By the way," he continued. "Tiny and all those boys work for the boss on the stud farm."

"Boys oh boys," Dan said.

"Tiny is the same age as me," Geoffrey went on. "Grew up on the stud farm. A bully all his life. The boss thought a spell in the navy would sort him out, but it only made him worse. He was on about you boys all night until I arrived, the darts players told me. All a bit of jealousy, you understand."

"Hope the boss hears nothing about the shindig," Dan said.

"You're joking," Geoffrey laughed. "There's nothing, just nothing, happens anywhere in these parts he doesn't hear about. He'll get a great kick out of that story."

T WO lorries arrived, one loaded with rough timber for shuttering, the other with sewer pipes.

"Why all the sewer pipes?" I asked Dan.

"Eventually they will be used for drainage," Dan said. He took the plan of the new pig parlour from his pocket. "Get an eyeful of this," he said to Jerry and myself. "This might prove useful knowledge one day." The plan showed a twelve-inch concrete wall with six-inch circular chambers from floor to ceiling, only three inches of a concrete facing, bridged by a three inch concrete rib.

"Very interesting," Jerry observed. "What's the big idea?"

"I brought this idea out in Mayo, just after the war," Dan said. "It's the answer to dampness. There's a vent top and bottom of each chamber, keeps the wall dry, saves the heat and will carry any type of roof. Sir Malcolm was quick to grasp this idea when he was over, that's why we're here."

"You're a proper caution, Dan," I said. "Maybe you'll tell us how you form those chambers."

"Simple," Dan said. "When the shuttering is complete, the six-inch pipes are placed faucet to faucet right round. The concrete is poured and after one hour the pipes are withdrawn, screwdriver fashion, clean as a whistle."

"It just beats Banagher, Dan," I said. "Did you ever think of patenting that idea?"

"I thought about it alright," Dan said. "The trouble is, how do you patent an idea? Sewer pipes and concrete were discovered a long time ago. The use of air as an insulator has also been known a very long time. Somehow it has never been thought of where concrete is concerned. At present if a fire occurs in a concrete building, the whole structure is usually only fit for demolition."

"I'd say Geoffrey will go a long way to alter that situation," I said.

"Geoffrey is learning fast," Dan said. "Mind you, I'm strongly prejudiced against concrete, except for dams or other engineering purposes."

"Okay for pigs, Dan," I said.

"Even pigs could live comfortably in a brick house. Economics, that's the lad, that's the architect," Dan said, folding his plans and heading for the site.

T HE flu which was causing havoc all over the country had at last paid us a visit. We had not been out all the week. George, of all people, was the victim. What Tiny or one hundred and one other Tiny's had failed to do, this invisible little monster had succeeded in doing. George was out for the count. For two days he had battled against it. "It could be a blessing in disguise," Dan said. "He was getting very restless. You two going back to London this evening would be the breaking point."

Geoffrey pulled up on his horse. "Heading back to the big smoke today boys?" he said. "I'm going to Bedford at three o'clock if you want a lift."

"Would you get me a bottle of Irish whiskey in Bedford?" Dan asked. "It's the only cure for that flu in the absence of the real stuff."

"Why wait that long?" Geoffrey said, dismounting and walking into the house. He returned a few minutes later with a full bottle of Jameson.

"See you in London," George said, as we called to say cheerio. Dr Dan was in attendance with the first instalment of 'the cure', a half pint of boiling hot whiskey.

"I have a message for Mrs Rogers," Geoffrey said as he brought the car to a halt. I jumped out and opened the big gates. Mrs Rogers, a stout good-looking woman came out to greet Geoffrey.

"Nan," Geoffrey said, "I've arrested these two highwaymen. You missed them with that gun on Monday."

"Heard who was in it," she said laughing. "We had a great laugh about that in the house."

Geoffrey entered the house with her. In a few minutes she returned with two large paper bags. "Now then, boys," she said, "slip into the orchard and fill these. I promise I won't shoot." Sheepishly we obeyed. Thanking her for being so kind, we were relieved to be on our way once again.

Geoffrey stopped outside the jewellers. "See you just around the corner in the Swan," he said.

The two girls greeted us gaily.

"Tell you what girls," Jerry said. "All the week I've been puzzling over what to get my girl friend."

"Did you come to a decision?" one of the girls asked.

"I did," Jerry said , looking at me. "I've decided

to get her an engagement ring."

"Good for you," the two girls agreed.

"You must pick me something different,"Jerry said, "otherwise we're all in trouble."

The girls produced a tray and after great deliberations a choice was made. Once again, after paying for the ring, we presented each of our helpful friends with a pear. They were still laughing as we waved goodbye from outside the window and went to join Geoffrey in the Swan.

D EIRDRE opened the door when I arrived with Jerry. She was in her dressing gown. "Had to go to bed," she said. "That stupid flu. I'm so sorry, boys, this is a terrible home-coming. I was hoping ye wouldn't be back till tomorrow ."

Not to worry, sweetheart," I said, "Jerry and I will get the fire going and sort out some grub. Where's Shirley?"

"Oh! she's not here," Deirdre stammered. "She left a letter for you, Jerry."

Jerry grabbed the letter from the mantelpiece and tore it open. Deirdre walked into the bedroom. The look of pain on Jerry's face spoke for itself. His eyes filled with tears, as he stood motionless. After a long pause he moved unsteadily towards the door, squeezing the letter into a ball between his hands.

"Jerry," I pleaded, grabbing him by the shoulder. "Please sit down and tell me what's going on." He shook himself free, whipping the door open, and staggered on to the street. Clearly he had made up his mind the matter was beyond talking about.

Deirdre was sobbing quietly as I went to the bedroom. "Poor Jerry. It's just terrible. No need to tell you who that letter was from."

"I guessed that alright, love, but please tell me what happened."

"Poor Shirley, I had a terrible time with her all the week. The fact of the matter is, she thinks the world of Jerry, but she doesn't love him. She's been trying to pluck up courage to tell him for weeks. A guy she was going with for a year came on the scene last week and that settled it. She's mad about him. He's in the resident band at Hammersmith Palais."

"I feel sick, love," I said. "I'll go out to the pub and get a cure for both of us." I would have to keep our engagement ring for a more propitious moment.

By Sunday, Deirdre had greatly improved. The shock of Shirley and Jerry was still uppermost in our minds. Jerry had not been at the digs, the landlady told us. Mrs Murphy and Tommy were deeply upset. More than anybody they knew Jerry's mind. Mrs Murphy made no secret of her special affection for him. Of all the lads Tommy Murphy had taken under his wing, Jerry was the one they talked about most. "A gifted pair of hands," was his summing up of Jerry. Tommy was not in the habit of lavishing praise.

"If only there was something we could do," I said.

"There is nothing anybody can do about a thing like this," Mrs Murphy said. "Time alone will solve his problem."

Deirdre felt well enough to return to work on Monday night. She was very upset to hear Jerry had not been to work. "Try his digs again," she said, as she rushed to catch her bus.

The landlady asked me in. "We're very worried about Jerry," she said. "It's not like him to stay away without telling us. Another thing, his best suit is in his wardrobe. He wouldn't go anywhere without that. My husband said he would go to the police this evening if he's still missing."

The fear that was running through my mind gripped me with something like panic. I would have to go to the police myself.

"I'm sorry to tell you," the sergeant said, "your friends body was recovered from the Thames this morning at Millbank. We found a letter on him addressed to his mother. The Civic Guards have been notified and his parents will know by now." I slumped down on the chair, too stunned to even think.

With their usual efficiency the Murphys took full charge. Meeting the parents; making arrangements with the undertaker; the church service and the final travel arrangements to Ireland. Both of them travelled to Ireland with the parents.

"Call for me in about an hour at Lyons Corner House," Deirdre said, as soon as the train pulled out. She walked to the back of the crowd to join Shirley and take her by the arm as they moved towards the street.

Chapter 10

"**I**'VE been with Shirley all afternoon," Deirdre said, as I arrived from work. "She's in a very bad way. I've had an awful job getting her to agree to go into hospital for a few days. She really needs help. I'm calling for her at seven o'clock."

"That's good," I said.

"Call and see her tomorrow evening on your way from work," Deirdre said. "I think you can help her more than anybody."

"I'll do what I can, love," I said. "In the meantime, you'd better take it easy."

"Don't worry," she said as she grabbed her coat. "The kids are no trouble at night."

Poor Shirley blamed herself for what had happened to Jerry, even though she could not possibly have foreseen it. Although she had gone through a rough time after falling out with the man she loved, she was the last person to think she herself would cause anyone to go to bits over her. To anyone who didn't know her well, Shirley came across as a true extrovert. To her close friends, especially Deirdre, she was self-effacing and unsure of herself. Small wonder, therefore, that the terrible tragedy left her bewildered and heartbroken.

The suddenness of it all left everybody floundering. I was personally sick at not having anticipated Jerry's total crack-up. The anguish and suffering of his parents was painful beyond words to all of us, but above all to Shirley. Deirdre really grasped the acute guilt Shirley felt and its consequences. How determined Jerry was that one day he would return to his beloved Leitrim. How tragic that it should happen like this.

It was a great relief to find the sister I knew sitting with Shirley, but she left as soon as I arrived. Shirley never even turned her head. In her hands she held a small folded religious tract, which she slowly kept turning over and over. I took her two hands in mine; no words were spoken. Deirdre arrived with tea.

"Now this is a right carry on," she exclaimed. "A damn good job I'm on duty in this hospital tonight."

"Get on with your work, nurse, remember your place and pour out that tea," I scolded. A faint smile creased Shirley's face,then faded again. We sat there for a long time with no word spoken.

"**B**LIMEY," Smithy said, as we sat at lunch some days later. From the quiet roadway two men came walking slowly across the clearing. They were long distance men without a doubt, but clearly not building workers. Their rough tweed trousers and very long jackets looked homespun and home-made. Both had the trousers tied around the knees with string, keeping the wide trouser legs well above the heavy nail boots. In Gaelic, one of them enquired if anyone had the language. The look of surprise on the face of Smithy and two more Englishmen at the fire caused Frank and myself to laugh. It was clear the visitors could see why. Frank motioned them to join us and had no trouble translating their story. They had been working for a farmer for three months and were heading for the boat. While they were sleeping in the open the previous night, near Watford, a gang of six young ruffians had attacked them. The gang, armed with daggers and flick knives, had robbed them of their savings. Their families were expecting them home and they needed work to get their fares.

There was little grub left to offer them. Smithy asked for a whiparound.

"You're the fastest man here." he said. "Slip out and get the poor bawstards something."

The whistle was gone when I returned. The two men were sitting on their own with a newly boiled can of tea. The sliced pan, the half pound of butter and the lump of cheddar got short shrift.

"Well that's that," Frank said, as he joined us on the scaffold. "Michael has given them the start. He's letting them sleep in the canteen."

At the weekly shop stewards meeting on Friday, a decision was taken to make a collection for the two visitors to enable them to return to their families. At finishing time on Saturday, Jimmy Ashcroft handed each of them twenty-one pounds. Up to now they had had no clue whatever what was going on. Frank explained things. The men were visibly moved. They would remember their visit to Twickenham for a long time to come.

T HE pointing was almost complete, and a good job too. No clothes made by man would keep out that November breeze. Next week it would be December. Only another thirty shopping days to Christmas. The nearer the time came the more uncertain I felt about the idea. Poor Jerry's enthusiasm, not to mention the others, had blurred any misgivings that crossed my mind. The house hadn't grown any bigger since I left and the family hadn't grown any smaller, but sleeping somewhere else would be a tricky business. A pure insult if I went to relations and proper bullshit, in the eyes of the neighbours, if I went to a hotel. No way would Deirdre get leave this Christmas. On the other hand the fever among the gang, bolstered up by Michael Coleman's encouraging remarks every Friday, wasn't easily shaken off. Then there was Shirley. Making progress but still in need of all the moral support she could get, especially around Christmas. I said nothing to the others about my mixed feelings.

In just two weeks, Shirley was well on the way to complete recovery. To my delight, she was at the flat on my arrival home from work. "Got thrown out," she said cheerfully.

"I've persuaded Shirley to stay for a few days", Deirdre explained. "Fantastic," I said.

"A friend of hers from the Savoy is calling later," Deirdre continued. "She has tickets for the Palladium."

"Just my luck", I said. "Wouldn't I just love to go swanking off to the Palladium with the three best looking women in London, instead of going to a Union meeting."

"You haven't seen Yvonne yet, you nit," Deirdre said.

"Well," I replied, "if she's half as good looking as Shirley, I'm still right."

"You go on to your meeting," Deirdre said, "we'll get on alright by ourselves."

I was about to reply when the door opened and Yvonne entered: a real English beauty with long blonde hair, hazel eyes and hardly any makeup. The three of us just burst out laughing. Yvonne looked as if she had just arrived from a long distance hiking trip. Strapped on her shoulders was a rolled up bundle, almost the width of the door. Under one arm was her handbag, under the other a carrier bag. Deirdre and Shirley jumped up from the table to help her dismantle.

"Tell me," I said to Yvonne, "why all the gear?"

"Oh!" she said, "that's my sleeping bag and some of my clothes." Sleeping bag! The thought flashed across my mind - just the job for me when I get home!

After the Union meeting Frank and I went to the Spotted Dog. Paddy the head barmen greeted us. "Friend of yours in the back room, wants both of you to join him."

Opening the door we gazed on the smiling face of George Logan, sitting alone, a full pint on the table before him. Frank and I sat down and burst out laughing. George had grown a beard, a black one. His hair too was jet black. " George," I said, "don't tell me Dan Lunn sacked you."

"Not a hope," he said. "I resigned. Another week down there and I'd be gone bonkers. Not too steady on the top storey for starters."

"I second that," Tommy Murphy said, as he walked in, followed by Jimmy, John and Peter.

"Dan will miss you, George," I said.

"You're jokin'," he replied. "He's doin' a big line with a widow down there. She's loaded, has her own house and a small farm. Not a chick nor child. Real jealous of her he is too."

"No wonder he was glad to see the back of you," Jimmy cut in.

"Many a true word said in jest", said George.

"Done a right job on the hair and beard," John said.

"Pays to have friends in the dye business," said George. "Believe it or not, Dan's woman supplied that , but she didn't know. Dan was helping her to mark a few sheep and got the brain wave."

"Would you doubt him?" Tommy said. "How's the job going?".

"He has two hundred pigs in residence already. When he's not visiting the widow, he's out drinking with his lordship. Wouldn't surprise me if he stood for Parliament down there."

"He was cross with me for leaving," George went on. "Told him I'd be back after I sorted out a bit of 'business'."

"Whatever the 'business' is," Jimmy said, "leave it till after Christmas. We're all heading for Paddy's land, you included. My ould mot has the turkey got already."

"Are you serious?" asked George.

"Of course I'm serious," Jimmy replied. "We're all heading for Holy Ireland, where a man can drink in peace during the holy season."

"Don't know what to think," George said. "Called in to see Nell on my way here, she tells me Colette is coming over next week." Frank Coffey and I finished our pints and ran for the bus. Hardly one word of my conversation with him registered, and I was glad when his stop came up. "Colette is coming over next week!" The words kept running through my mind. I could see her face before me all the way home.

Shirley decided to go to Blackpool for the remaining days of her sick leave. "Let's pray things work out for her," Deirdre said. "She really is crazy about that man."

"Things should be very quiet in Blackpool at this time of the year," I remarked. "Wouldn't you think he'd come to London instead? He didn't even think it worthwhile to come and see her when she was sick."

"Maybe he would have, had he known," she said. "He's getting a week off in two weeks time. We'll see plenty of him then."

"Can't wait," I said.

"Don't be such a doubting Thomas," Deirdre said. "If Shirley loves him, he must be a nice bloke. She's nobody's fool."

TWO weeks before Christmas Ann,Deirdre and I came out of the cinema to find a sudden drop in temperature outside. The bus skidded on the icy road and took ages to reach our stop. By the time we got to the flat we were frozen.

"A cup of tea would really go well," Deirdre was rushing for the kettle before we had our coats off. Then she let out a groan,staring in dismay at the frozen tap. Ten minutes of burning newspaper brought no response.

"My God," Ann said. "If this thing keeps up 'twill be disastrous. Let's hope the forecasts are all wrong. Just imagine what it would be like at the hospital."

Ann's fears, alas, were only too real. Water became a priceless commodity in the days that followed. Everywhere there were burst mains and burst boilers. The black bitter frost penetrated through windows, doors, walls and roofs. Cars and even buses were abandoned and forlorn. The bus services were in total disarray, the Underground jammed. Droves of pedestrians slid to and from work in silence. Greater London with its teeming millions was almost powerless to come to grips with this silent unrelenting marauder.

Deirdre and Ann had no option but to stay put at the hospital. Frank moved in to keep me company. Bed to pub and back to bed was now the compulsory routine. "Don't know what gives way first, the frost or the money," Frank remarked.....

A fearsome screech woke me up in the small hours. Frank stood framed in the adjoining doorway, water still cascading from the ceiling onto his bed. A sodden blanket was wrapped around his shoulders and water dripped from his shirt tails.

"Mother of God," he muttered, more to himself. "That tear's the arse out of it good and proper."

"Come in and close the door," I yelled. Paralysed from cold and shock he paid no heed. Reluctantly I jumped out of bed, whipped the soaking blanket away and flung it back on the waterlogged bed. Still cursing and muttering to himself, he staggered around, then lifted the flimsy bedside mat and started to wipe himself all over. Though only too conscious of the shock and horror in store for the girls, I couldn't stop laughing, and covered my head with the bedclothes to wipe out the crazy scene.

My laughing abruptly halted however, as Frank slid into the end of my bed. His feet were like a pair of frozen lobsters. I could only pray the girls would have some way of bringing frozen mummies back to life.

Roll on Christmas!

"**I** 'LL never go into a 'home going' scheme again," I told Deirdre and Ann, as we made our way to Paddington Station.

"You'd never have gone otherwise," Deirdre said. "It's dead lucky Ann can stay with me and Tommy is getting leave as well."

"Just as well Michael Coleman and the timekeeper arranged to collect all the tickets," she went on. "If those boys got their hands on the money, they'd be plastered and half of them wouldn't see the boat."

"Better be careful with Yvonne's sleeping bag," she continued.

"You can rest your mind about that, love," I assured her. "That's the best invention since the submarine."

Ann folded her paper. "I'm half sorry I came along," she sighed. "Paddington Station always makes me homesick."

"That stupid weather is game to the last," I moaned.

"Don't worry," Ann said. "Once you get out of London, it will be sunshine all the way."

The railway bar was already crowded. "Be careful with your luggage," Michael was moving around, giving advice to everybody.

"I'm dying to see will poor Colette get George on that train," Deirdre whispered.

"It's a fifty-fifty one that," I replied. "There's one thing for certain, nobody else only herself would stand a hope."

"I'll believe it when I see him waving from the train," Ann said laughing.

"So long as the boys in blue stay away, the chances are good," I said.

"If you ask me," said Deirdre, "they will stay away if they think he's bailing out for good."

Even though there was still over an hour to go before departure, the station bar was buzzing with excitement. A young Dublin plasterer I knew as Joxer, had started to play the uilleann pipes. It had occurred to me he was a musician. His mastery of the pipes was evident from the start. He was joined by two whistle players. A huge man called Finbarr, known as 'The Gentle Giant' on the job, came through the door with his two mates. The three hailed from near Boyle. Finbarr in his new suit and without that cap he always wore peak backwards, was a really fantastic specimen of humanity. He had a great resemblance to Jack Doyle, but was a bit taller and heavier. As they came to a halt at our table, it was evident the three had been celebrating.

"Watch here," Finbarr said. "Are you all travelling?"

"The girls aren't, Finbarr," I replied.

"That's too bad. Wherever did you get those lovely girls?"

"Won them in a raffle, Finbarr." Ann stood up to grab three stools that had been vacated.

"Take a seat, boys," I invited, "and I'll fetch a drink."

Before Ann could take her seat, Finbarr caught her under the elbows and raised her over his head. He swung her around a few times as the musicians raised the tempo. A big cheer went up as Finbarr swung to the middle of the floor, lowering Ann in case she collided with the chandelier but still holding her off the floor. Then, giving her a big kiss, he put her down and they walked back to our table, both laughing.

"Ah! come on to Boyle," Finbarr said, addressing Ann. "The crack will be ninety over there for the

Christmas. My ould one would be delighted. Nobody left now only herself."

"Give us a song, Finbarr," one of his mates requested. The musicians were taking a break.

"Can't sing for nuts," he replied.

"Don't mind him," his two mates protested.

"Come on," Ann demanded.

Finbarr took his pint from the table and quite casually drank it in one go. It was obviously not a once off thing, nothing at all strange to him or his mates. None the less, from the surrounding tables, a great laugh went up.

"Roll on Boyle," he shouted. "I've waited nine years for the sight of a good black pint."

"Give us that song," somebody from another table shouted.

"Up Kerry," someone shouted from further up the room. An old man with a squeaky voice immediately shouted back "fuck Kerry". It was some minutes before the hilarious laughter died down.

Ann and Shirley had returned from the bar with a tray of drinks. Finbarr loosened his tie and commenced to sing 'The Old Rustic Bridge by the Mill'. Everybody joined in the last verse of the song. There was a great cheer and cries for more.

"Well look at who's here," Deirdre said, jumping to her feet. Looking over my shoulder I saw the beaming face of Frank, and, standing beside him, Ranter. A different Ranter, accompanied by one of his now soberly dressed companions. Gone were the exotic clothes and hairstyles. They were dressed like hikers, with dark polo-neck sweaters and heavy boots. Both had hikers' bags strapped over their shoulders.

"You're really going home, Ranter, and I'm proud of you," Deirdre said, shaking his hand. Ranter laughed. "By the sound of things here," he said, "Christmas has already started."

"That pub out in Praed Street is jammed," Frank said, as we both went to the counter to get drinks. The uilleann piper and the whistle players, now joined by a concertina player, were once again making the rafters ring with a medley of reels.

As we returned with the drinks, I noticed a good-looking woman in a fur coat come through the door. She stopped at our table. "Are you with Michael Coleman's party?" she asked.

"That's right," I replied.

"I want to speak to him, but I don't know him. Could you find him for me?"

"Of course," I said, as I spotted Michael at the far end of the bar. Michael shook hands with the woman, ushering her away from the noise, out to the reception hall.

"Who on earth is she?" Deirdre asked.

"Haven't a clue, darling," I answered.

Looking through the open door I could see them both. The woman was doing all the talking. Michael looked pale and shocked.

"What the hell is she going on about?" I asked.

Michael left the woman and took some faltering steps towards the door. He beckoned me to join him.

"Bad news," he whispered hoarsely. "Get through there and ask the musicians to wind up."

When the music stopped, Michael began to speak: "I must ask everybody present to be prepared for a shock. This is Mrs Featherstone, the wife of the timekeeper. Mr Featherstone left the house yesterday morning to go to the bank and didn't return. Mrs Featherstone notified the police early this morning, but so far there is no news of his whereabouts. I don't need to spell out the seriousness of this situation. Not only the money paid in all year, but the week's wages and overtime money, was all in his care. I feel too sick to say more. The consequences for all of us about to travel are just disastrous."

Mrs Featherstone was sobbing, slumped on a chair provided by Ann. Apart from that, there was a deadly silence. Michael Coleman stood with his hands over his eyes, quite obviously in great distress. Slowly, around the room, a number of girls could be heard crying. A voice from nowhere asked: "Does this mean we can't go home?" Nobody answered.

"We must all be fucking mad," somebody said aloud at last.

"Not going home?" another voice said incredulously.

A pint glass went flying through the room, smashing against the mirror at the back of the counter. Michael jumped on a chair, holding his hands above his head. "Let us for Christ's sake, not lose our heads."

"We've nothing else to lose," a voice shouted. Tense as the situation was, this remark caused a ripple of laughter.

"We'll be the laughing stock of London," a man shouted. "Thick Paddies. Gobshites, that's all we are."

The barman looked on apprehensively. Nobody was ordering a drink. Everybody seemed to be glued into inactivity. The uilleann pipe player was dismantling the pipes, placing each part carefully in the case.

Once again Michael stood on the chair. "I am going along to the police station with Mrs Featherstone," he said. "I would like if two or three of you would accompany us. Meantime, please try to stay calm. We'll be straight back to report whatever the latest news is."

A sudden commotion outside the door caught everyone's attention. Agitated voices of women and men could be clearly heard. A tall man appeared in the doorway, blood trickling from his nose. "There's fucking murder outside the station," he roared.

Instantly there was a mad rush for the door, causing tables and chairs so be overturned; glasses crashed off the tiled floor. "Whatever is wrong out there," Ranter said, "they're mad to rush out without weapons." Like lightning, both he and his companion were smashing the legs off stools and tables. The barman stood behind the counter dumbfounded.

"It's them and us again, that's for sure," Ranter

said as we gathered the weapons thrown in a heap beside the door. "Carry them under one arm," he ordered. "You'll need the other arm free if we're attacked.

O NLY minutes had elapsed since the call for help. The sight that met our eyes outside was frightening in the extreme. At least half a dozen battles were raging simultaneously all over the street. The whole of Praed Street was jammed with spectators, and black marias were lined up on both sides of the road. Some yards to the right, a car, turned on its side, was ablaze.

"Throw the weapons over the coppers' heads," Ranter ordered. Two policemen came charging towards us, their long batons held high. A shriek came from Ann as they attacked. Ranter and his friend had both policemen disarmed without even using a weapon. One of them was now on his knees, the other lying face downwards.

Moving past the policemen behind Ranter and his mate, Deirdre gripped my arm. "There's George," she cried.

To the left of the entrance, George Logan was standing with his back to the wall, Colette beside him. Grim as the situation was, the sight of Colette startled me.

Lined up on both sides were more than a dozen of the Willesden crowd, including Jimmy and John Palmer, Frank Coffey and Mickey Flynn. Finbarr and a gang of five or six were crouched, tiger-like, waiting for another onslaught. A huge roar went up as a black maria went tumbling on to its back at the Praed Street end. Within seconds, lighted matches and cigarette ends were being thrown on it from all sides. Suddenly it burst into flames. People scattered in all directions, their hands over their eyes.

Colette had spotted us and had slid along the wall behind the men. She was now standing with Ann and Deirdre. "They were determined to get George," she said hoarsely. "After all my work. Blast them."

"Listen, Colette," Ann said tersely. "There's no way the police will give up. This battle will go on until they get George or he manages to get away."

"Can't see him escape this time," Colette said.

"There's one slim chance," Ann said. "It's possible to get into the grounds of the hospital from the back of the railway station."

"I doubt if George will agree," Colette said. "He'd rather die than desert his friends."

"For God's sake," Ann sharply retorted. "His friends will be mangled if he doesn't get lost. Go quickly and talk to him. All it needs is a big commotion and it could work."

"That's no problem," Ranter said. "Go and talk to him," he told Colette. "Ann is right."

Colette slid away. Soon we could see her in a huddle with George, Jimmy and Bill Ryan. Ryan looked at us and nodded. It was clear the plan had been accepted.

Once again Colette was back. "That's on," she whispered. She slipped away to our right and succeeded in reaching Mickey Flynn and a large group who were on the far side of the road. The sudden activity, the to-ing and fro-ing, soon became apparent to the police. Highly trained in crowd control, they knew from the signs that some new move was afoot.

The shrill sound of approaching black marias heightened the already desperate tension. Suddenly a large crowd, Mickey Flynn in their midst, rushed two of the stationary black marias. The two vans were sent tumbling on their sides, the police jumping clear just in time. Bottles, glasses and lumps of masonry came soaring towards the police from all directions.

"Deirdre and I will lead the way and do all the talking," Ann said, as George and Colette reached us. "Ranter and his friend will come with us to the end of the platform in case we're stopped." George nodded. The six moved towards the main entrance. "Try not to get arrested," Deirdre whispered as she left.

"Ken and I will be back in five minutes," Ranter promised.

Three loud blasts from the mighty steam engine, lasting a full minute, drowned out the noise in the street. "There she blows", Frank said. "Wonder what time the next one leaves?"

"Next Christmas," I replied.

Once again a lull had set in. The loud-hailer van had arrived. "Please pay attention," the booming voice announced. "We call on all present to surrender peacefully to the police. The whole area is surrounded."

"Withdraw the police and we'll go home," a man's voice shouted.

Ranter and Ken returned. "They made it," Ranter whispered. "The message is, if yourself and Frank can get to the hospital, ask for Nurse Collins."

Fog had now reduced visibility to about ten feet. The smoke and fumes from the burning vans was now almost unbearable. "Listen," Frank whispered. "The reception hall is crawling with police. They've come in from the back."

"I can see one chance of escape," I said. "That burning van on the right is so close to the wall they won't expect anyone to fly through there."

"Worth trying," Ranter whispered. "You two make the break and we'll follow."

Slowly we edged our way as close to the van as the heat would permit. "If we make it, see you all at the Spotted Dog," I whispered.

Only split seconds separated the four of us as we plunged through the burning debris of the van. So far the ruse had succeeded. The group of police on the far side of the street were taken completely by surprise. About half a dozen batons came flying through the air, one catching me on the shoulder. Switching down a narrow street to my left, I soon realised I was on my own. The fog had now worsened.

Half an hour later, reaching the Harrow Road, I was greatly relieved to see the trams still running. Finding a seat at the rear of the top deck, I gratefully settled down in the semi-darkness, my heart still pounding. My mind began to race over the last few hours. There would surely be great disappointment in the house, to say nothing of the worry and speculation. Who would have suspected the timekeeper, so much a part of the company, and to all appearances a happy, stable, settled pillar of respectability. One thing was certain. If I lived to be ninety, I would never again trust anyone with my savings....

F ROM the outset, I had had mixed feelings about the trip, especially with Deirdre unable to travel. At least the timekeeper had solved that problem. But I felt sorry for all the others. Their plight was bad enough without that diabolical fracas in Praed Street. How many would end up in a cell over the Christmas was anybody's guess.

The couple in the seat in front of me suddenly stopped hugging and looked over their shoulders for, without realising it, I had laughed to myself. Yvonne's sleeping bag! Worse still, my new Marks and Spencers suitcase with my brand new Burton suit so carefully packed by Deirdre, with all those shirts and underclothes - all gone! Clearly some sinister power had decreed I should never wear a suit or take charge of a suitcase under any circumstances.

"Willesden," the conductor shouted, "'appy Christmas, all you lucky people."

The Spotted Dog was like a beehive. The evening papers already had the story on their front pages! 'STREET VIOLENCE OUTSIDE PADDINGTON STATION' 'THREE POLICE VANS SET ON FIRE' 'BUILDING WORKERS CONNED BY TIMEKEEPER' 'TRIP TO IRELAND FOR CHRISTMAS OFF'

Battling my way to the counter, I had to look twice to make sure my eyes weren't deceiving me. Maybe my head had gone astray. Standing together as if nothing unusual had happened were Mickey Flynn, Peter, and John Palmer, all deep in conversation. Noticing my astonishment, all three burst out laughing.

"That shook you," Mickey said.

"Can't believe it," I muttered.

"Handy things, taxis," Peter said dryly.

"We saw ye making the break," Mickey said. "A few minutes after that, two trains arrived. One from Glasgow and one from somewhere else. There was pandemonium as the crowds spilled out of the station. Between that, the fog and the fire brigade, the cops gave it up as a bad job. It's doubtful if they got anyone."

"Hope they don't check the hospital," I said, which reminded me to go to the phone.

"We'll be leaving soon", Deirdre said. "George is being kept in for a day or two. Concussion. The three of us are going back to the flat, so don't be late."

My heart was light as I put down the phone. It had been a day of terror, but my friends were safe, and I would be spending Christmas with Deirdre.

Chapter 11

MICHAEL Coleman was not surprised that most of the lads decided to leave the job. No doubt they all felt as Mickey Flynn, Frank Coffey and myself, that to continue there would be a constant niggling reminder of our holiday debacle. An architect friend of Mickey, who at one time had ambitions to become a professional boxer, now specialised in renovation work. His firm had widespread contacts, a stroke of luck that was most unexpected - most fortunate too, because the weather after Christmas was simply odious. Fog, rain, snow, frost, in ever-changing cycles, made ordinary building work a hopeless proposition.

Mickey had also become heavily engrossed in the boxing club, so much that he inveigled Frank and myself to join. Most of the lads were Cockney, dead keen, and on the whole, great mates. A week after joining and having a number of lessons from Mickey, not to mention long sessions on the punch bag and spring ball, he allowed me into the ring for my baptism. Baptism is right. It nearly proved to be my wake. My opponent, Fred, was an Eastender, a bit younger than me, with a Cockney accent that even most Cockneys couldn't understand. We became very good friends from the outset. Mickey was in the ring barking instructions and, in my case, giving a constant reminder to "keep the gloves closed and guard your chin."

For the first two rounds I did well. Then momentarily forgetting Mickey's advice, I caught a

haymaker right on the chin. How long I was in the
land of nod, I'm not sure. Mickey's voice and the
background noise seemed very distant.

"You did great," he said casually, when I sat up.
"You'll have to work hard at that guard."

"Now," I said to Mickey, in a very serious tone of
voice, "when can I expect a crack at the British
Title?"

Fred Hill felt more of a foreigner around these
parts than any Irishman or Scot. Mickey took a
great shine to him and gave him a job tending
Frank and myself, with a promise he'd get Tommy
Murphy to give him a break on the tools later in
the year.

BY a freakish coincidence our first job was in
Cork Street, less than a minute's walk from Mr
Stein's shop in Savile Row. During the lunch
break, I suggested a walk in Berkeley Square,
which meant passing the shop. The photographs
were still displayed large as life. Fred and Frank
turned back as I stood to gaze. The famous
uniform, my delivery bike, it all seemed such a long
time ago.

"Gor Blimey," Fred said suddenly, "that geyser
looks a ringer for you."

We were in fits laughing when the door opened
and Mr Stein appeared, looking highly amused.
"Glad you like my picture," he said.

"Yeah," Frank said. "He looks so like our mate
here."

Mr Stein took a step nearer, catching my arm

and turning me to face him. Then he pushed my cap to the back of my head. "Upon my word," he said very quietly. "How slow of me. We often wondered where you'd got to. The Illustrated Paper Exchange is now huge. Got branches all over London. They've moved their head offices to the Strand, I see them regularly."

"This is a turn-up for the books," he continued. "Wait till I tell your boss, Mr Cameron."

Frank and Fred looked on in bemused silence. "Must get you to make me another suit, Mr Stein, when I get rich."

"That's a deal," he replied.

"No use making him a suit," Frank said, as we moved away laughing. "He keeps on losing them."

"I'll make you a suit," Mr Stein said loudly as he waved goodbye.

"Got a very tricky job in Oxford Street," Mickey announced as Cork Street neared completion. "A ladies' dress shop. The snag is they want to carry on business as usual. Means working some nights as well as Saturday and Sunday."

"If it's got to be done, it's got to be done", we all agreed.

"I'll give ye a hand," Mickey went on.

Not only did the shop sell dresses, one window had a display of fur coats, long and short, plus a variety of stoles. Instantly I made up my mind: If my luck holds out, I'll give Deirdre the biggest surprise of her life.

Strange how Oxford Street so quickly quietened down after the shops closed. By six-thirty only a sprinkling of window gazers were moving about. As I carefully hacked at the old brickwork on the window reveal, I saw reflected in the glass, a figure standing behind me in the street. The reflection clearly showed it was a nun. Since the windows were empty I thought it strange anyone would want to stop and gaze. Sheer curiosity made me stop hammering and turn slowly to confront this over-curious onlooker.

Staggering off the low hop, I stood shaking and speechless as an impish smile creased the beautiful familiar face.

"I recognised you instantly...." she began.

"Eileen...." I said, in a hoarse whisper." Eileen......"

"'bout time you said hello," she laughed.

I moved out to get away from the hammering and in the next doorway gently put my arms around Eileen and hugged her. There was no way I could suppress my tears.

"Have you much time, Eileen?" I stammered.

"Well I've just got back from Ireland," she said. "They allowed me home to my mother's funeral."

"Isn't this the most incredible encounter?" she went on, as I averted my eyes, unable to suppress my feelings. "I was on my way to Bayswater Road. "I'm staying there with the sisters tonight, and tomorrow night, and travelling to Folkestone on Monday.

"Will you come for a cup of coffee with me, Eileen?" I asked.

"Love to," she replied, "if you can get away."

"Get away?" I said emphatically , "I'd break out of Dartmoor to hear that voice. Listen boys," I told Frank and Fred, "can't explain now, you'll see me when you see me." Before they could answer, I went waltzing up the street with Eileen.

"Listen mate," I began, as we settled down in the Express Dairy cafe. "You have no right to endanger the life of an old china."

"Your Cockney is improving," she said.

"This ticker of mine will never get back to normal, that is definite."

"Not to worry," she said. "I'll say a little prayer for you every night."

This remark shocked me into the realisation that this joyous encounter would be painfully short lived.

"I'm so sorry to hear about your Mammy, Eileen."

"The family is totally shattered," she said. "My superiors were kind enough to let me stay at home for two weeks. Nothing will ever be the same again."

"Tell me Eileen,"I asked. "Why did you change your mind about being a nurse?"

"Ah! but I didn't," she laughed. "The thing is, this way, I am fulfilling a double ambition." She flicked the silver crucifix on her breast, engraved with a tiny red cross.

"Tell me all about yourself," she requested. "Are you happy at the building work?"

"Very happy," I replied. "I always wanted to be a tradesman and I love the bricklaying."

"Bricklaying?" she said, looking puzzled.

"Oh!" I said. "This renovation work requires a lot of hacking out."

"Mrs Diver, Arthur and myself were really lonely after you," she said.

"I'll tell you the honest truth, love," I said, "I just lost the head completely. How I didn't wind up under a bus is something I will never understand." Instantly I could have kicked myself for being so stupidly theatrical.

"We did decide at the time you had jumped to a ridiculous conclusion. The fact is you were wrong. The man I went to meet that night at Speakers Corner was my first cousin. He was going through a very serious crisis. From the moment he joined the Guards he realised he had made a terrible mistake. Like myself, he had always been discouraged at home about achieving his true ambition. He wanted to talk things over with me. After going through a very bad nervous breakdown, he got his discharge and is now studying for the priesthood in Maynooth."

For a long time we both sat there unable to speak. Eileen slowly moved her hand over and gripped mine.

"The past is the past," she whispered. "Only the future is important. That's what mother always used to say. Tell you what", she said. "Do you know the little church in Marble Arch?"

I nodded. It was the tiny church I had been to with Colette.

"I'll meet you there at ten o'clock Mass! Afterwards we could go for a walk in Hyde Park and maybe get a good laugh at Speakers Corner. Now, if you can spare the time, will you walk with me as far as Bayswater Road?"

I stood trembling as the large wooden doors closed behind her. Retracing my steps unsteadily, I had an overwhelming urge to fly home there and then to tell Deirdre of this incredible experience. In all the world, she alone would understand. Dear kind, loving Deirdre. Without her to go home to and share my thoughts and feelings I would once again be walking the streets aimless and lost.

Kneeling at the back of the tiny church I watched the remote-looking slim figure kneeling in the front row. Who would believe that inside that austere black gown, a heart of pure gold was throbbing?

I waited in my seat till the people had left and Eileen came down the narrow aisle to join me. The warm sunshine had encouraged great crowds to make for the Park. After all the fog, frost, rain and sleet, the opportunity to get out and about was irresistible. Having walked right through the Park we decided to explore the adjoining Kensington Gardens. How such a vast area of greenery had survived in this sprawling metropolis, was surely the eighth wonder of the world.

"Tell me," said Eileen, as we found an unoccupied park bench. "Have you still got that famous uniform?" We both broke into laughter.

"You'll have to agree it was the smartest uniform in London at the time."

"I'd say, any time," Eileen said. "Don't tell me

you haven't preserved it?"

"It's like the Lartigue Railway, Eileen," I said. "Gone but not forgotten. All that remains now is the belt and the photograph in Mr Stein's window."

"Oh!" said Eileen, "Mr Stein wasn't the only one to have that photograph. Mrs Diver got one too."

"I wouldn't doubt her," I said, hoping the subject would go no further.

"Guess what I'd really love to do."

"No idea," I replied, as casually as I could.

"I'd just love for both of us to call and see the Divers."

My reaction was so apparent that Eileen kissed me on the forehead.

"Eileen, my love, you wouldn't do a thing like that to me," I said pleadingly.

"Not to worry, just thought it would be fun," she said.

"Tell you what," she went on. "I have more money than I'll spend in the convent for twelve months. Let's go and have lunch on me. There's a nice place next door to Whitleys."

"Great," said I.

THIS was getting dangerously close to Westbourne Grove. My instinct told me Eileen had not abandoned her plan to visit the Divers, with or without me. As we reached Whitleys corner a number fifteen bus came cruising towards us. As it pulled up at the bus stop, a mad impulse caused me to grab Eileen and push her on the bus. The conductor stood before us greatly amused at our outburst of laughter. "Wish I knew the joke," he said, deliberately ignoring the proffered fare. "Wish all my customers were as cheerful," he said, as we jumped off, only four stops away.

If only he knew how far from cheerful I felt. My knees buckled and my heart began to pound as we climbed the steps to number two hundred and seventeen.

Arthur opened the door. The shock at seeing us rendered him speechless. He staggered back opening his mouth to call Mrs Diver, but no voice came. Arthur was in his shirt sleeves and had on a pair of rubber gloves. He was obviously engaged in some domestic chore.

"Blimey," he croaked, as Mrs Diver put her head around the door. She pushed to embrace both of us, and ushered us into the living room.

"If you both planned it for months ye couldn't have picked a better time," she said, as we apologised for our unheralded visit. "Guess what? Roast beef and Yorkshire pudding! You've both changed so much. I'm so excited I'll have to sit down and take a glass of port. Just tell me all about yourselves, the joint will be another half an hour."

Eileen told her of her sad trip home. I told her of the sad trip I *didn't* make home.

"Arthur has a lovely job now," she said. "Commissionaire at Whitleys, no travelling. Paddy is now a sergeant. His battalion is doing guard duty at Buckingham Palace. Maybe ye'll come to the Changing of the Guard this afternoon."

"That would be lovely," Eileen said, casting a glance in my direction.

THE unexpected sunshine had brought a huge crowd to sample this much-vaunted tourist attraction. The colour, splendour and clockwork precision of the guardsmen all added up to a really unique ceremony. Every move made by Paddy, every order he barked, meant a sharp dig in the ribs from Mrs Diver. She was truly proud of her nephew. "That must have brought great memories back for you Arthur," I said, as the parade ended.

"You can be sure of it," he said. "The very same thing happened every day in the viceroy's palace. Over the years I couldn't count all the times I was involved."

Mrs Diver and Arthur had arranged to meet Paddy after the parade.

Eileen had to get back to the convent. I waited for her while she collected her things and travelled to Victoria Station to see her off. Saying goodbye to a loved one is never easy. Parting with one so lovable, with not even a remote chance of meeting again, was agony indeed.

IN spite of my absence without leave, Mickey Flynn soon forgot his annoyance. The bricks had arrived and everything was going according to plan. In his spare time, Fred Hill was excavating a deep hole in the small yard. This was to be the first of many private air raid shelters our little gang became involved in. Such was the tension brought about by events in Europe and the general foreboding heightened by the daily headlines that shelter mania had gripped London and no doubt every other city in Britain.

Everybody, including the architect, was delighted with the new shop front. The manageress was most excited about her window display for the sale, to coincide with the new front. "Any bargains going tomorrow," I asked her casually.

"Have a look at that," she said, handing over the latest issue of Vogue. Encircled in pencil was an ad: 'June in January. June Furs, Oxford Street, big sale to coincide with new opening. Irresistible Bargains'.

"The first customer in the morning will have a seventy-five pound coat for fifteen," she said.

"How early would you expect the first arrival?" I asked.

"Very hard to say. The last time we had a sale, two girls stayed up all night. Depends a lot on the weather."

My mind was already made up. Telling Deirdre that Frank and I had to remove some scaffolding and clear up before seven o'clock, I set the alarm clock for five. I arrived at the shop at six fifteen and was astonished to find the place lit up, and the manageress and her three assistants busily engaged arranging the two windows. Right in the centre of each window was a short leopard skin coat, the label showing the old price, seventy-five pounds, with a big line through it. 'Sale Price Fifteen Pounds.' My arrival caused great amusement. The manageress opened the door.

"Miracles will never cease," she said laughing. "Slip in the back and make a pot of tea."

"Don't want to miss my place in the queue," I said.

"Don't worry, you won't."

By the time the tea was ready about a dozen women had gathered outside.

"Now then," the manageress said, "I take it you're interested in the leopard skin?"

"That's it."

"Any idea of the size?"

Already I had studied the girls. "That's as near as makes no difference," I said indicating one of them. They all laughed. The manageress went in to the shop and returned with a coat. The girl slipped it on. The fit was perfect....

With my precious parcel under my arm, I ignored the escalator at Oxford Circus Underground. Descending the stairs, four steps at a time, I would just make the flat before she left for work.

Deirdre was still in her dressing gown having her usual hurried coffee and toast, a puzzled look on her face.

"I've got it," she said, pouring me a cup. "You had a row with Mickey."

"Miles out, try again."

"The woman skipped with the money?"

"Wrong again," I said laughing.

"Somebody robbed all the tools?" Suddenly looking at the clock she jumped up. "You nit, I'll miss my bus..."

Drawing the swanky bag from inside my raincoat I stopped her in her tracks. She held the shimmering garment at arm's length, her eyes fluttering in stunned surprise. With tears appearing, she flung her arms around me, still holding the jacket.

"Try it on," I said. "If it's the wrong size, I'll have to get back fast."

Throwing off her dressing gown, she donned the jacket and did a modelling pose in her scanty negligee. We both fell around laughing.

"I can't believe it," she said. "You're pure mad!"

"Runs in the family. Come on quick or we'll both be sacked."

"Can't wait to tell Ann," she said, as we sat in the tram. " I've already made up my mind. I'll not wear it till my final exam party and then guess what?"

"Too late for guessing, honey, it's my stop."

Dragging me back she whispered, - "then our honeymoon." I threw her a kiss from the street as the tram pulled away.

"HAD a phone call today from Shirley," Deirdre said, as I got in from work. "They're coming up tomorrow and she suggested meeting them at Hammersmith Palais. Ken is standing in with the band."

"Try anything once," I said.

Shirley was waiting in the foyer when we arrived. The dance was in full swing. When we found a table, she waved towards the stage.

"That's him," she said, as Ken nodded in our direction. We all laughed at this unusual introduction. Shortly afterwards he moved to the microphone and gave a virtuoso performance on the saxophone. Altogether different in appearance to what I had imagined, Ken was tall, broad-shouldered and very good looking.

Slipping away from the band after his stint, he ushered us back stage apologising profusely for being tied up. A variety of drinks was on the table. "Help yourselves," he invited. "We'll have plenty of time for a chat later in the hotel."

"We booked a second room provisionally," Shirley said. "The hotel is only ten minutes walk from here. Do say ye'll stay the night."

"Impossible darling," I said. "No pyjamas."

"You can have my sleeping bag," Shirley said.

"No, Shirley," Deirdre corrected, "*I'll* have the sleeping bag."

"Fight about that later," Shirley suggested. "The important thing is ye'll stay. I want ye so much to get to know Ken."

Most members of the band and their girlfriends arrived back at the small hotel. Ken was a personal friend of the proprietor who gave us a great welcome. "We always have great sessions here," Ken said. How right he was. Almost everyone had a special party piece. Anyone called on by the proprietor who failed to perform was duty bound to buy a round. A compelling incentive, I decided, as I made a gallant effort at 'When Irish eyes are smiling'. This set off a medley of Irish songs, the words and the airs surprisingly familiar to this mostly English gathering. By three o' clock the girls, Ken and I were glad to make our escape. After a goodly ration of John Jameson, any dispute regarding the sleeping bag or pyjamas was now purely academic.

"He's a nice guy," I murmured sleepily to Deirdre my eyes already closed.

"Told you," she said.

We said no more, but as I went to sleep I was thinking about poor Jerry Fitzsimons.

Chapter 12

ARRIVING home from work the next day, I was surprised to find the flat empty. Puzzled and not a little worried, I put the kettle on the gas. Could be an emergency, I concluded. Must be something serious to keep her back at work.

A moment later Deirdre arrived. Ann was with her.

"Didn't know there was a tram strike," I said, by way of greeting. "Would you look at that fire," Deirdre moaned. "That's carrying the saving act a bit too far."

"If I don't get a speedy explanation from you two, there's no fire and no tea."

"Well, if you must know, Ann and I went for a drink and a little chat. We girls do have things to talk about."

"Oh! that's a perfectly good explanation," I interrupted. "Makes a nice change I suppose."

"I'll make the tea," Ann said, "while you too get on with your love affair."

"Will one of you tell me what's going on?"

"It's like this," Deirdre said, a perceptibly serious tone to her voice. "We had our routine medical today, and I've been ordered to see the specialist tomorrow afternoon. They take no chances with important people like us."

"A truer word you never said," Ann said. "Don't you know ordinary mortals will never understand that?"

"Nothing to get worried about whatsoever,"

Deirdre said. "Routine, you understand."

"What's the idea of the specialist then, that's hardly routine?" I persisted. "What sort of a specialist is he anyway?"

"The doctor discovered a lump on my breast, she's just playing safe. I tell you there's nothing whatever to worry about."

"You didn't know about this yourself?" I asked.

"I certainly did not," she retorted impatiently. "I've told you it's just routine. They leave nothing to chance."

All that night, as I pretended to be asleep, I knew Deirdre was pretending too. I was still awake at eight o'clock when a factory horn not far away disturbed my thoughts.

ARRIVING home after a day I thought would never end, I was more than pleased to find Deirdre and Ann busy preparing dinner. A bright fire was blazing.

"Ann insists on treating us to a night with Clark Gable," Deirdre said cheerfully.

"Never mind Clark Gable. How did you get on with the specialist?"

"Won't know the result for a day or two," Deirdre said casually. "Anyway, I'm taking a week's leave. Poor Ann is back to the grindstone in the morning."

All though the picture a nagging fear prevented me from taking any great interest in the amorous exploits of the world's number one heart throb.

M Y fears were heightened when Deirdre returned from the phone two days later to announce Matron would like her to call to see her. My fear changed to shock and foreboding when she told me the surgeon had advised an operation without delay. I decided to take the rest of the week off work.

Four hours after the operation, Deirdre still remained gently sleeping. "She'll come 'round after a short time now," Ann whispered. "It will help her a great deal to see both of us here. Once she gets out of intensive care, everything will soon come right."

The surgeon called and indicated there was no need for me to leave. After a brief examination he left, accompanied by Ann. In mortal fear of how Deirdre would cope with the aftermath of this dreadful calamity, I sat by the bed too scared almost to breathe. I took her hand and gently stroked her bare arm. Opening her eyes, she slowly turned her head and smiled.

"It's all over darling," I whispered, kissing her on the lips.

"I'm dying for a cup of tea," she whispered back.

"The best news I've heard in my whole life," I replied, as Ann appeared with a tray laden with a silver tea pot, milk, sugar, and three cups.

I T soon became clear, in the days following the operation, that Deirdre's recovery was far from satisfactory. Her brave efforts to cover up her true feelings were painfully obvious. Besides, Ann's prediction that she would be out of intensive care in two or three days had not come true. Waiting for Ann in the hallway, I was now determined to know the truth. In my wildest dreams, I was unprepared for the bombshell. Tests and x-rays had borne out their worst fears. Another operation would be useless.

"Has Deirdre been told?"

"The surgeon has told her," Ann said, in a faltering voice. "No point trying to hide the truth from Deirdre."

Too stunned to speak or move, wanting to be sick, a cold shiver caused my mind and body to go completely limp.

"My God, Ann," I said at last. "What are we going to do?"

Ann slowly shook her head. Then, holding my hand, she whispered. "We owe it to Deirdre to show the same courage that she has shown. Go in now."

The terrible days and nights dragged on. Friends came and went, making heroic efforts to carry on conversations. Deirdre bravely endeavoured to respond. Long hours were spent with only the two of us, hardly saying a word. I knew her thoughts, like mine, were going back over all the happy days and nights. How we had laughed about poor Arthur. The great fun at the dances. The laughs at Speakers Corner. The strange encounter with Ranter and his friends. Ginger and all the excitement of her wedding. The jokes, the joys, the happiness, the traumatic brush with the police at Vauxhall Bridge Road. Too well I knew similar thoughts were coursing through the mind of the gentle uncomplaining girl I gazed upon. No need for words now; no more stories; no more songs; no more scoldings; only complete union of mind and thoughts. I held the outstretched hand - "I love you" - the whisper was so faint.

So softly had Ann entered the room, I was unaware until I felt the gentle touch of her hand on my shoulder. She bent over to kiss Deirdre.

"Look after him, Ann," I heard.

Then Ann's sobs told me the long struggle was ended.

T HE hearse came to a halt outside the huge wrought-iron gates. A line of cars pulled in behind. From a single-deck bus, nurses in uniform came hurrying forward, all carrying flowers and wreaths. They lined up on either side. Any time now I would wake up and realise all this was a mad dream. People were moving around talking in whispers.

Back at Murphy's now, the house was crowded. Mrs Murphy handed me a sleeping tablet and a glass of water. "You must get some sleep." I had forgotten the meaning of the word.

The events of the last six weeks were still hammering at my brain when Mrs Murphy appeared at the door. "Good man," she said, "get yourself dressed. It's time you got something to eat. Ann stayed here last night as well. She has to leave in half an hour."

Ann poured out her tea and mine, nodding her agreement with Mrs Murphy's well-meant insistence that we both eat breakfast.

"We'll both see Ann to the bus," Mrs Murphy announced. "Tommy will be in any minute now."

"I must get back to the flat," I stammered.

"Not a good idea at all, at all," Mrs Murphy said emphatically.

"I must go back. I have something important to do. Tell Tommy I'll call back tomorrow. I really have to go. Don't worry," I said in a feeble effort to assuage her indignation.

No words were spoken on the way to the bus stop. When our bus arrived Mrs Murphy gave Ann a quick hug and a kiss.

"Are you sure?" she asked as she turned to me, her eyes moist with tears. I kissed her on the cheek and whispered, "don't worry." She walked quickly away as we scrambled on the bus.

T HE fire was made up, ready to put a match to, and the rug turned upside down. Everything was tidy. There was a bowl of fruit on the table. I stared around feeling like a first-time burglar must feel on entering somebody's flat. My nerves were at breaking point. Must get that box from the bottom drawer in the bedroom. The box was safe and sound under the carefully folded underclothes. No need to count it, I remembered only days before that 'routine medical', Deirdre had announced: "we now have one hundred and seventy pounds. Enough to cover our wedding and plenty left over

for the trip home." And she had waltzed into the
bathroom, singing. I wondered why she sang in
the bath, considering nobody could get her to sing a
note outside of it. Not even when we were alone.

All tenners. I would have to take one, wrap the
rest in a page of that magazine. God, would I ever
get out. After a quick look around, I took the
photograph from the mantelpiece. That and my
working clothes would do; no way was I ever
coming back. I wrapped the trousers, coat and
jumper in left-over wallpaper, tied with my I.P.E.
belt, all that was left of that famous uniform. I left
the fur jacket; Ann would help Frank to sort
things out. I slammed the door and staggered onto
the street. Maybe a walk would clear my brain...

I was at King's Cross station. How long had I
been walking? The bar was crowded.
"A whiskey," I said to the barman. After all the
walking I was still freezing. The whiskey made me
cough violently.
"Try a drop of water, maite," the barman said in
a friendly way. Instead, I ordered another whiskey.
A couple vacated a nearby table. I sidled over
and sat down.
So many things to do. Must give Murphys a rest.
Will return tomorrow and sort things out.
Hopefully the money will be enough to cover the
funeral. I must get out of London - anywhere. A
trip home! Maybe there will be enough money left
over. I had a sudden compelling need to see them
all, especially my mother. How well she would

understand.

"Blimey, you was quick off the mawrk." I vaguely felt the woman was addressing her remark to me. "'e's not even listening," she continued, addressing a second woman carrying a stool. They both settled down at the table.

"Just sayin', Ber, 'e was real quick off the mawrk."

"Oirish, I'll bet my life, am I roight duck?" Ber said nudging me gently. "'e's the quiet type, Dot, you can see that. Isn't that roight, duck?" I nodded my head. "Course I'm roight!"

"Get a drink, Ber, it's your twist." Ber headed for the counter.

"'arry told me what you was drinkin'," Ber explained, placing a whiskey in front of me.

"You're awlright my old maite," she said brushing off my show of surprise. "Not long over 'ere then?"

"A good while now," I replied.

"Knows loads of Oirish people, we do," Ber went on. "Always get on well with the Oirish, isn't that right , Dot?"

"Never met a bad un yet," Dot readily agreed.

The wine was low in their glasses. "Same again, Harry," I requested, as Harry came to the counter.

"Blimey, we didn't want another drink." It was Ber's turn to protest.

"Ah! well, a bird never flew on one wing," Dot said. "'ere's to the next one. You 'aven't told us your naime."

Both of them laughed heartily when I obliged.

"Real Oirish, I'll be blowed," Ber exclaimed. Why I had given them the Gaelic version I wasn't sure.

"Last drinks!" Harry shouted. "The wee kid is weeting yonder." He put on a mock Scottish accent.

"'old your 'orses 'arry," Ber interrupted. "Just three small uns, then we're off. Blimey, we'll 'ave it down before the rest of this shower realise it's closing toime."

Waving his fist, Harry instantly produced two small ports and a small whiskey. Ber and Dot grabbed their handbags, Ber flinging a pound on the counter. "Tell you what," Dot called for hush. "Tell you what. I'll get a bottle of plonk and we'll drink it back in the boardin' 'ouse."

"You're a proper genius, Dot," Ber said. "Never thought you 'ad it in ya."

"Will you lot take a powder before I lose my rag." Harry was standing over us, glasses piled one upon the other, from the waist to well above his head.

"Stone the crows," Ber cried, jumping up. "Don't drop that lot, we're on our way."

"Where you stayin' then?" Ber asked as we reached the street. I waved my arms and took a slight stagger.

"Blimey," they both exclaimed. "That whiskey 'as gone to your 'ead. Take 'old of 'im Dot. We'll get 'im a cuppa and a sandwich back in the boardin' 'ouse. It's only down the street, duck. You cawn't go nowhere till you sober up a bit. Isn't that roight, Dot?"

"Course you're roight," Dot agreed. Already we

were progressing slowly towards the boarding house.

Two middle-aged couples who had been playing cards collected their money and rose from their seats as we entered the small living room.

"Don't let us disturb you, duckies," Ber exclaimed. "Plenty room for everybody."

"Should have been upstairs hours ago," one of the women said, to murmurs of agreement from her companions. "Nighty-night Mr Fowler," they called to a man who now appeared at the door. "Thanks for everything," one of the men said, as they filed out. Mr Fowler looked at me and took a step forward, closing the door behind him. Without speaking, he indicated he wanted an explanation.

"Took a chance inviting the young man back in the 'ope you'd give 'im a room," Ber said quickly. "Felt a bit poorly awfter a few drinks. Not used to it, that's the trouble. Dot and I thought maybe...."

"Alright," Mr Fowler cut Ber short.

Rising to my feet I muttered "sorry", and made to leave. Turning at the door to say goodbye, I swayed forward. Mr Fowler put out a hand to steady me.

"Very well," he said. "I'll fix you up with a room."

"You're a brick, Mr Fowler, and that's the truth," Ber burst out. "We both knew you'd understand."

"Bed and breakfast is seven and sixpence. That suit you?" I nodded.

Mr Fowler invited me to follow him upstairs. I was glad to see the lavatory at the end of the short corridor. I glanced through the bedroom door Mr

Fowler had opened, then rushed to kneel at the pan, banging the door behind me.

I heard the sound of shunting trains, cars passing under the window, Ber and Dot still chattering on their way to bed. Strange how people can sleep through all this noise. Neither the noise nor the blinding headache could stop the scorching thoughts flashing through my mind.

Soon I heard the grating sound of the first tram only feet away from the window and saw flashes from the overhead cable darting across the ceiling. Time to be on my way.

Mr Fowler tapped on the door. "Breakfast now being served."

Dressing quickly, I suddenly realised I'd left the bundle of working clothes in the pub. And the money?! I searched my pockets, a mad search. Panic gripped me. My head reeling from shock and disbelief. The change from the tenner was all that was left in my trouser pocket.

"One hundred and sixty five pounds! Are you serious?" Mr Fowler repeated. "You can't be serious. What the hell would anybody want to carry that much money around for? One thing is certain, nobody in this house would touch anything. If you're not dreaming then all I can say is you dropped it in the pub. You were rightly on when you arrived here last night and that's putting it mildly."

I placed three half crowns on the table."The dining room is through there," he said.

"I don't feel like eating," I replied. " I must get

some fresh air."

THE pub was still closed. Dense traffic, impatient drivers sounding horns, added to the din. Tourists were feeding the pigeons in Trafalgar Square. I took a walk along the embankment. More tourists were boarding a boat for a trip to London's dockland. An old man took a seat beside me on the wooden bench. He seemed anxious for a chat. "Streuth to God, nobody wants to talk anymore. Gets borin' up in that room. Sometimes I envy the poor bawstards down 'ere at night."

"Mostly Irish," I say.

"Not on your life, from all over."

Not far away I halted once again. A cloud of dust hung over two refuse lorries, the sun rays causing countless silver dots to flash and disappear. A gang of men were ambling to and fro from the huge arch with an assortment of rags, paper, cardboard, tins, bottles and cans, even a foul-smelling shoe box, dripping excreta. I sat on the parapet wall to watch this strange operation.

"Enjoying yourself?" one of the men asked sarcastically, as the lorries were about to move away.

"Hard work," I replied, taken aback.

"Thanks to you scruffy fuckers," he yelled, jumping on the running board. I didn't bother returning his soldier's farewell...

Chapter 13

THERE was a short queue outside the Salvation Army Hostel. A uniformed soldier-of-God was barring the way to three highly agitated callers.

"Caused trouble once before," he yelled in a high pitched voice.

"If you was 'arf a man I'd smash your ugly puss in," one of them shouted back. His two companions grabbed him and they moved away, the aggressive one still hurling curses. I file in at the end of the queue. Plates of porridge were being distributed by two girls in uniform. What am I doing here? I wondered, feeling the money in my pocket. Must be going stupid.

A gong sounded. A tall man was standing at the top of the room. He placed a bible on the table before him. "My friends, you and you alone, possess the power to insure your future in the Kingdom of the Lord Jesus Christ." The girls had now joined him, one on either side. The voice droned on. Nobody made a sound. I replaced my spoon quietly and rested my head in my hands.

The money. Any hope of recovering it in the pub was completely ruled out. I must wait and talk to those women. How could this stupid predicament be explained to anybody, especially the Murphys?

I could hear Big Ben; still only eleven. The voice no longer droned. My fellow diners had left without me noticing. The girls were now clearing the tables.

"Decided to leave you finish your prayers," one of

them said. "Captain was in good form this morning."

"I apologise for being late."

"Not to worry, friend. Come any time the need arises. Be guided by the Lord, Alleluia." She gently closed the door behind me.

Harry was chatting with two customers when I arrived. I took a seat at the end of the counter. "Find any money last night after we left?"

"Money," Harry said. "What sort of money?"

"One hundred and sixty five quid in notes," I replied.

"You off your chump, Paddy?"

"Off the chump is right, but I still lost the money."

"I changed a tenner for you, I remember that alright. Blimey, one hundred and sixty five nicker. Hear that?" he yelled to the two at the counter.

"We 'eard", one of them replied. "Must 'ave plenty to be throwin' that kind of money around."

"Listen, Harry," I spoke quietly. "I left with those women last night."

"Now you're really tearing the arse out of it," he said sharply. "Take my tip and rule that idea out, good and proper. That's dynamite, you understand? Wouldn't take a penny if they was starvin'."

"No intention of accusing them. No harm in talking to them about it though...."

"Just markin' your cards, Paddy. Watch how you approach things."

"Mind if I sit around?" I asked.

"Blimey, that's okay. I'll get you a drink. Help yourself to the bread and cheese."

M UCH as I nursed the pint, I still had a long time to kill until six o'clock.

The pub was now filling up quickly. Men rushed in grabbing a quick pint, others settled down. Four men were busy at the dartboard. Harry waved me to the counter and put a pint in front of me with a plate of bread and cheese.

Making for a table, I noticed for the first time a large charcoal drawing on the wall: the familiar figure of Sherlock Holmes, with Dr Watson in the background carrying a tray of drinks. Pity the great man wasn't around last night I thought. I was still admiring the picture when I heard the familiar voice of Ber.

"Gor Blimey, Dot, will you look at 'oose 'ere." The two took a seat and shouted their order to Harry. "Stone the crows," Dot said cheerfully. "We thought you was 'eading off this morning. Didn't like disturbin' you, did we, Ber?"

"No way," Ber agreed. "We was out soon awfter 'awf past seven. Did they look awfter you alright?"

"Somebody looked after me good and proper. I lost a big sum of money."

"You wot?", Ber said. They both gazed at me looking really puzzled.

Harry rushed over with two glasses of wine and a fresh pint. " 'e's told you," he said, casting his eyes around.

"That's torn it," Ber said at last. " 'ow much we

talkin' about?"

On hearing the figure, Ber leapt from her seat, her glass of wine toppling onto the table.

"Easy, Ber," Dot said. "Take it easy maite. 'e didn't say 'e blamed us."

"It's a flamin' shock just the saime," Ber replied, resuming her seat. "When did you miss the money then? Cawn't get over it, no way." She was talking more to herself. "Dot will tell you we've lived in that 'ouse over five years now. Never once 'eard of a penny goin' missing."

Harry returned with a new glass of wine and wiped the table. "Bloody awful", he said, "and I'm thinkin' bloody stupid as well."

"I should have moved on, just couldn't go without telling ye," I said, in an effort to ease their agitation.

"Never could save up," Ber said, "so I wouldn't know what it's like to lose any."

"Makes you feel like gettin' sozzled," Dot said."Blimey. A small fortune."

"Call another drink, Dot," Ber told her. "Just as well we've 'ad our grub."

"I must go." I said, getting to my feet.

"Don't be dawft," Ber grabbed my arm and pulled me back on the chair. "We're not short of a few bob. Besides 'arry is always good for the slate. Ain't that right 'arry? Get 'im a whiskey, Dot, 'es partial to a small un."

The two women were kindness itself. I was satisfied beyond a doubt, whoever had the money it wasn't them. Determined to escape while I still had the use of my legs, I promised to return some time and repay all their kindness, then staggered through the door, too confused to decide whether to turn right or left.

T HE cool breeze from the river was a welcome relief. The shimmering water reflected the great array of lights on the far embankment. Reaching the wooden bench I had shared with the old man, I lay down undecided and confused. Almost before my mind had begun to work on what to do, a torch was shining in my eyes. The tall figure of a policeman stood over me.

"Just having a rest", I stammered.

"No loitering along 'ere after dark," he said sternly. "If you must rest, move down under the bridge, otherwise I'll 'ave to take you in."

I was sorely tempted to ask him to do just that. Instead I got to my feet and headed to where the cloud of dust had caught my attention, what seemed a long time ago. Already the area under the bridge, dimly lit by a flickering street lamp, was stretched full length covered with an assortment of old coats, rags and cardboard.

Feeling tired and exhausted I sat down at the entrance. At least it would give me time to think. Putting my head between my knees, I once again realised how stupid I was to forget those working clothes. Tomorrow I would write to the Murphys, go to the Labour Exchange and get out of London. Otherwise I would expect to see her at every familiar spot, cropping up wherever I met our friends. Far away from the old haunts and the old friends, I would settle down with the precious memories. Just her and me.

My thoughts were suddenly interrupted by the shrill sound of approaching sirens. Four wagons stopped, their headlights brightly illuminating the grisly scene. Loud orders from a dozen policemen: "Now then, let's be 'avin' you. We 'aven't got all night." What this was all about I couldn't even guess and little cared. The wagons were now backing up, doors wide open. Clambering on before my fellow dossers had roused themselves, I sat quietly wondering what would come next.

As our convoy pulled away I could hear more wagons arriving, the combined sirens splitting the midnight air. People for miles around might be excused for thinking that Hitler had just invaded the land of hope and glory.

We tumbled out on to a huge square surrounded by three-storey buildings. A queue was already forming at a large door.

"Strip to the skin, 'and your clothes in and give your name and last address." The Belmont Institution flashed to my mind. There at least men queued to get in. The compulsory shower was the same. Not so the huge dormitory. Beds were lined along both walls and up the centre.

"What's it all about?" I asked the man in the next bed.

"Just bullshit," he replied. "A mad notion they get when there's a full moon. Seems they found a body under the bridge this mornin' covered with rags. All bullshit you understand. Poor bastard probably died of hunger."

Men were ambling up to a row of buckets at the end wall and urinating.

"What's the game?" I asked my friend.

"More bullshit," he replied. "They keep the door locked in case we wander in our sleep."

"Wish I'd known, I'd have moved a lot further down."

"They'll all settle down pretty soon," he said consolingly. Then, after a short pause, he said quietly: "Don't look now. I spoke too soon - a head banger."

I heard heavy breathing behind me and slowly turned my head. A thick-set bald-headed man was standing stark naked not more than two feet away. How stupid I was to take the end bed. Obviously crazy and muttering incoherent sounds, the ape-like creature edged slowly forward. The closeness, vulgarity and sheer obscenity made me wonder had I really gone mad. How come a raving lunatic like this hadn't long ago wound up in a padded cell. A man had now jumped out of bed and was pounding the locked door yelling for the orderlies. My mind numbed with revulsion and anger. Almost by instinct, I lifted the flimsy blanket and let fly with my right foot, instantly somersaulting onto the floor, in no doubt what my fate would be, should he get his hands on me. Before I had regained my balance the crazed figure lurched forward, fell to his knees, and vomited all over my bed.

By now men all over the room were banging the

walls and the iron bed-heads with their shoes.
Shocked and petrified I backed towards the door
where the other man still banged and shouted
furiously. The bald head still slumped over my bed
told me my aim had been dead on target. Though
the room was now in pandemonium, I knew I was
in mortal danger when this crazed sick creature
recovered.

Suddenly the door crashed open, sending the
shouting man and myself sprawling. Four
orderlies, batons at the ready, thundered in, two of
them making straight for the shouting man and
myself.

"Hold it," the man yelled. "Get that baldy
lunatic out of here."

There were shouts of agreement from around the
room as the other two orderlies approached Baldy,
pushing him unceremoniously on to his back.
Then, grabbing one foot apiece, they dragged him,
still horizontal, through the door. Once again the
door was closed and locked. I rescued my coat and
trousers from the end of the stinking bed and
stretched out along the wall glad at least the
heating pipe was still warm.

LYING on the floor, the terrible trauma of the
last six weeks was coursing through my brains.
Even the mad events of the last two days,
including the loss of the money. An added spur, as
if one was needed, to pull myself together and get
out of London.

Once again the door swung open. "Rise and

shine," the orderly shouted.

"What happened the nut case?" my friend asked.

" 'e's been taken into custody," the orderly replied. "Blimey, 'e's only out a week after doin' fifteen years. Fancy lettin' 'im loose with money to buy drink. 'e strangled the poor bastard they released with 'im."

I left the dormitory and moved to the front hall with my friend. As I did so, my heart stopped. My nerves suddenly caused pins and needles to freeze my head and face, as I came face to face with Ann and Jimmy.

"Say nothing," Jimmy said quietly. "Let's get out of here."

Ann grabbed my arm as we moved down the street to a cafe. "The cops called at Murphys at seven o'clock this morning," Ann said as Jimmy went to the counter.

"I was mad to give them that address. I didn't want them snooping around the flat."

"Mrs Murphy got an awful fright. That's why we're here. Tommy insisted Jimmy came with me. All's well that ends well."

Before I could apologise, Jimmy was back with the tray. "Any harm in asking what goes on?" he asked casually. "What are we trying to prove?"

A knowing glance from Ann confirmed what I already sensed. Jimmy was in no mood for flimsy excuses. "Did it occur to you, people would be worried?" he continued. What he or Ann would say if I mentioned the money caused me to shudder.

"Put it down to madness," I stammered. There

was silence for some seconds.

"I must go," he said, drinking back his coffee. "You're acting the so and so. Just cut out the theatricals and give us all a break. See you Ann," he snapped as he put his cap on and disappeared through the door.

For a long time we both sat without speaking. "Just as well it's my day off," Ann broke the silence. Once again I was tempted to mention the money.

"Deirdre made one request she.... wants you to have her fur coat." Another long silence. "I feel like a walk," she said....

HARRY was taking in a delivery of beer as we passed the pub. "Watch 'ere," he shouted as we came up. " 'ang on a minute!"

With some reluctance, Ann followed me into the bar.

"On the road early," he remarked, giving Ann a sly look. He reached under the counter and drew out a bundle of clothes. "Might need these," he said, throwing it in the air for me to catch. As I grabbed the bundle, a small package went fluttering to the ground. The wrapping came loose, tenners scattering over the floor.

"Bloody 'ell," Harry blurted out. "Stone the bloody crows!"

All three of us were now standing over the scattered money, a look of sheer puzzlement on Ann's face.

"Picked the lot up myself when I was cleanin' up. Under the table beside the other lot. Blimey, I thought it was a tie or a pair of socks."

"Can't get over it, Harry," I said. "I really had given it up as a bad job."

"Blimey," he exclaimed, putting three glasses on the counter, "we'll celebrate that bit of luck with a drink. "What a pity Ber and Dot aren't 'ere to celebrate with us."

"How right you are," I agreed, peeling a tenner from the bundle Ann had picked up and tidied. "A fiver for yourself and a fiver for the girls to celebrate tonight."

"Blimey, we'll all have reason to remember this coronation."

"Do try and get back tonight," Harry said as we took our leave. "The girls will be mad if you don't."

Ann was quiet as we walked towards Trafalgar Square. "That really takes the biscuit," I said. "Wouldn't herself do some scolding. All the plans we had. One hundred and seventy pounds, Ann, most of it her doing, I needn't tell you."

"I gather the money was lost," she said quietly. "I can also understand how excited you must be at finding it. I'm just puzzled about the girls Harry was on about."

Grabbing Ann by the arm, I stood in her path and for the first time in more than six weeks, burst out laughing.

"What's so funny?" she said, evidently upset and puzzled.

"For crying out loud, Ann," I said, putting my arm around her shoulder. "The 'girls', Ber and Dot, are both older than my mother. Real friendly old

Cockneys that did everything to help me when I got jarred. They were real upset when I discovered the money was gone. Let's take a bus to Oxford Street Ann. We'll get lunch at Lyons Corner House. So many things to talk about. Then if you want to, we'll go back to the pub and meet Ber and Dot."

"I know how you feel about getting away," Ann said, as we settled down to lunch. "That's how I feel too. I've applied to have my leave brought forward. I'm just dying to get home."

"Listen," she continued, as I nodded agreement. "Why don't you go home to Ireland and see your family? You really look worn out and the change will do you the world of good. We'll do a bit of shopping and you can still get the train this very evening. What do you say?"

The suddenness of the idea made me laugh nervously.

"Come on," Ann said decisively. "You need a new suit and the rest. You can't walk into your mother in that state after all these years."

We walked arm in arm down Oxford Street towards Selfridges. In no time I had a new suit, new shoes, shirt and tie, a new military-type mac, enough underclothes as well as a warm jumper for my mother and a pullover for my father. Tucking them all away in a new sleeping bag, we struggled in to the customers' cafe feeling well entitled to a break from hard work.

"We'd still have time to call back and see Ber and

Dot," I suggested.

"No way," she said. "This is one train you are not going to miss...."

Chapter 14

T HE thought of meeting all the family, the fuss I would cause, how my mother would react, preoccupied me on the train, the boat and the second train. My heart was pounding as we came to a noisy halt in Listowel. Scrambling out, I prayed nobody would recognise me.

Right in my path, his head tilted to one side and a roguish grin on his face, stood the unmistakable figure of Roger.

"I don't believe it," he gasped. "It couldn't be. Is it really yourself?"

"Right first time, Roger. You haven't changed a bit."

"Well 'pon my soul, but you're the man that has changed. Only I know the family so well, I'd never have guessed who was in it. How long is it?"

"Five years, Roger."

"Boys, oh boys. Tell me, are they expecting you?"

"I didn't write, making it a big surprise."

"No doubt about it, but they'll be proud of you. Let me take that bag."

"If anyone sees you carrying my bag, Roger, they'll really have something to talk about."

"Don't mind them hobos, you should be proud of yourself. A self-made man and no doubt about it."

How glad I was nobody else had taken Roger's attention. His great technique and unbridled flattery acted like a tonic.

"You're making loads of money over there. I hear you're on the buildings."

"Not doing too bad, mind you, Roger."

"This town has gone to hell altogether. Anyone that's any good has left it. A man wouldn't get a day's work unless he worked for nothing. I'm seriously thinking of baling out myself." Roger steered me in the direction of Scanlon's bar.

Downing his second pint in one gulp, "I must fly now, or I'll miss the Limerick bus, he said with a wink, "You'd never know who'd be on it." Then with a string of blessings, he rushed through the door. I purchased ten Woodbines, a message long overdue, and headed for the taxi.

T HE mile to the junction of the Forge Road took John Guerrin only minutes. "Turn the car here," I told him.My hope of a quiet approach was soon shattered. This new Kerry Blue I'd been told about in my letters had as little time for strangers as his illustrious predecessor. Opening the door, my father soon brought the excited animal to heel. Then, with a stunned expression on his face, he moved sideways to let me in. My mother was kneeling at the form beside the fireplace, a rosary beads in her hands. I had arrived in the middle of the rosary.

"Don't let me disturb the good work," I declared, as my mother rose to her feet trembling all over.

At first I thought my eyes were deceiving me - something to do with the now unfamiliar light from the oil lamp. I started laughing at my own crazy notion, and both of them joined in.

"No wonder you'd laugh," my mother said at last. "The house must surely look comical after London."

"It's not the house that makes me laugh," I quickly assured her. "I just can't believe it. You both look so young."

"Forty two and forty three," my mother said laughing. "Sure we're nearly fit for the pension." Then, more seriously, she said: "We're so sorry we couldn't go over for the funeral. Did you get the letter?"

I nodded. "I couldn't answer it."

"I know. Didn't you come home yourself instead? That's much better."

"You'd swear I knew you were coming home," she went on. "It's ages since I baked a currant loaf."

"My lucky day," I told her, as I placed the tray on my knee.

Without a sound, a tiny figure in a long night shirt, sidled past on my left. Another slightly bigger figure, similarly attired, appeared on my right. Without yeah or nay, they settled down on the wooden blocks either side of the hob.

"Mother of God," my mother exclaimed. My sudden outburst of laughter sent the tray and all its contents tumbling from my lap. The Kerry Blue could be heard throwing a fit outside the door, as my father yelled and grabbed the tongs to retrieve the cup, saucer and plate from the fire.

"Meet the last of the Mohicans," my father said, as my mother set about replenishing my tray.

"I might have known," she said, "the day couldn't end without those two buckos causing ructions."

"Two real highwaymen," she continued. "Maybe you'd take them off to London and sell them to somebody. Come to think of it, you might take your father as well."

"Watch your step, Missus," I warned. "There's women over there would give their eye-teeth for a man like him."

"Now you're telling me," she retorted. "If I'd known that, I'd have packed him off with the Black and Tans."

"The others will be in soon," my father told me. "They're all fine. Phil and Aine won't know you at all, they were so small when you went away, Now, boys, back to bed."

"Hold on," I said, as I unfolded my sleeping bag and handed them their presents. "Wait till I show you my bed."

All four went into convulsions, as I crawled into the bag and stretched out before the fire.

"A great invention," my mother said. "If only I had thought of that idea long ago."

No amount of giving out could quell the hilarious laughter of the two boys after they returned to bed. All apprehension about my home-coming was now well and truly laid to rest.

"No hope of sleep after all that excitement," my mother said, as she stacked up the fire.

"What have you done with his nibs?" I asked, catching sight of the Brud's photograph above the fireplace, revolver in hand, where De Valera for so long had held pride of place.

"Oh," she said a sad smile creasing her face. "Gone with all our great hopes and dreams. Once again it's a crime to talk about the 'Cause'. Once again Republicans are back in jail. Now, instead of taking to the hills, the youth of the country are heading for the emigrant ships. The great dream that kept us going is now buried under a welter of greed and selfishness. In spite of all the danger it was wonderful to be alive while that great flame engulfed us all. If only we had remained united, how different things would be. Our final hopes dashed with the broken promises of 1932. Hopes dashed before the bonfires and torches had flickered out. I'm afraid," she said, lighting a cigarette, "the hate and the bitterness will be around for many a day."

"What the hell am I on about?" she said, grasping my hand. "It's great to have you home. Tomorrow is another day. One great consolation, the children are not saddled with bitter memories. It's great to see them all happy together and playing their football."

"What became of Billy?" I asked. "It's years since I got a letter from him."

"He joined the army," she said. "That fellow was always dying to get into a uniform."

NEXT day my mother, Phil and Aine arrived home from town laden with parcels. I had been left to mind the house and become acquainted with four-year-old Eddie and two-year-old Seamus, not to mention the new Rebel, who still treated me with suspicion.

The two dozen stout and the bottle of whiskey spoke for themselves. "Dick is bringing out the

melodeon and Paddy Mahoney the fiddle," my
mother said, after she got her breath back. "Also
Nixey and a few of the neighbours. It's ages since
we had a bit of music in the house."

Before the music had even begun, half a dozen
neighbours made sure of a seat.

"Music fit for a King," Nixey summed up the
general feeling.

"Yerra, what King?" my mother exclaimed.
"They never heard the likes."

Like all great nights, time went by at a gallop.

"I declare tomorrow a national holiday," my
father said, as he headed for bed long after
midnight.

A FTER much coaxing, but with a distinct lack
of enthusiasm, Rebel did condescend to join
me on a ramble late the next day. We walked to
the Furry Glen, then along the river, skirting the
town, and in to Gurtenard. Birds everywhere were
vying with each other as if engaged in a great
competition. Memories both happy and sad came
crowding in. Thoughts of Angela, my earliest sad
loss, reminded me too much of my latest one. It
was time to retrace my steps.

My visit to Gurtenard was only one part of a
double trip I felt impelled to undertake. My
enquiries about the Brud had been too hastily side-
tracked to leave any doubt there was a conscious
effort to cover something up.

"That man is worse than Jackie the Lantern,"
my mother gaily side-stepped my enquiries. Jackie

the Lantern was the ultimate in elusive folk characters, a specialist at luring unwary travellers away from their intended destination on the misty flat regions of the mountain. His lantern first appeared close to the much dimmer light of one's destination, then kept flashing into view that bit further away, leaving travellers bewildered and disorientated. As children we had believed in him just as we believed in Santa Claus.

I made my way to the house in Church Street where the Brud now lived with his young wife and family. Approaching the house I found a young woman standing in the doorway. "Are you the Brud's wife?" I enquired. The young woman laughed.

"Yes, I'm Cathy. Only it's too obvious who you are," she said, "I'd be tempted to say no. So many people call here to take him out, I have a full time job answering the door. Do you realise how much you take after him?" This remark flattered me greatly.

"We heard you were home," she went on. "The Brud said you'd surely call. He should be back any minute. You picked good weather anyway. It was a terrible winter. Poor Brud hardly got outside the door."

I refrained from answering, my worst fears confirmed by this quite casual remark. No doubt she thought my mother had left me under no illusion what to expect.

"There you are," she said, interrupting my thoughts. "The bould hero is on his way. He must be psychic."

Again I made no reply. Walking slowly towards us on the far side of the street I saw what looked like a feeble old man. A long overcoat hung loosely on him, buttoned to the neck. Only the jaunty cap, the peak low over the eyes, the crown pushed high up, gave any clue as to who was in it.

Coming to a halt opposite us, the Brud stood for a minute before crossing the street, a big smile on his gaunt face.

"A sight for sore eyes," he said, as he reached us, "We knew well you'd call."

"I should fink so an awll," I replied, putting on my best Cockney accent.

"Blimey, don't remind me of that kip. Come and see the baby," he invited, leading the way in to their ground-floor flat where a girl of about fourteen sat rocking a baby. Cathy introduced the girl as a neighbour's daughter.

"Well, well," the Brud said, "tell us about yourself. Your mother tells me you're making great strides at the building. Should be no trouble to you after working for the Hannons."

"Never mind all that," I cut in. "Why don't the three of us slip out somewhere and have a drink."

"I second that," said Cathy. "It's not every day we have something to celebrate."

Brud was still in his overcoat, despite the strong evening sun beaming through the high window. Walking to the dresser, he took a large glass dish in both hands and placed it on the table before me. It contained a dazzling collection of silver and gold medals, the slanting sun caused them to sparkle and dance as the Brud fumbled through them. Picking one of them from the dish he handed it to me, I assumed for me to admire. It was inscribed on the back 'County Championship 1927'.

"Keep that," he said, brushing aside my protests. "You carried my bag often enough to merit a far bigger reward."

Tongue-tied and embarrassed, I was unable to speak. Cathy quickly sensed my predicament.

"Quite right," she said. "Besides, only for poor Gran, not one of these precious medals would we now have."

"Right," said the Brud, "put your coat on, woman, and stop giving out."

John R.'s was almost full. The hubbub of conversation noticeably dropped as we entered. John R. came from behind the counter and, with a nod of his head, quickly plucked two high stools from beneath two customers to seat the Brud and Cathy. The move was made so discreetly that Brud never noticed.

John R. was a towering figure of a man, as big as Steve Casey or Rex. His deeds of strength and skill on the sportsfield were legendary, not to mention his unrivalled record in the struggle for Independence.

Immediately to our right three men stood in conversation. "That's the Courier's son," I heard one of them remark. The nickname was a calculated insult. I decided to talk as if I hadn't heard.

"That's two of them so-and so's," Cathy whispered. "Bitter as ever, and thick as ever."

Like a flash the raid on the Lodge came back to me: the taunts and insults hurled at my mother, the threats against the absent Brud. For the vast majority the hatchet was well and truly buried, the awful nightmare laid to rest. People from both sides of that great sadness were now fully occupied with the struggle for existence.

"Couldn't have luck, the same fucker." The voice came through clenched teeth beamed at the Brud's ear. Brud quickly put his pint on the counter, his feeble arms pushing Cathy and me aside as he moved a pace forward to confront his tormenters. Before the Brud had time to speak, Big-Mouth lifted his cap, holding it by the peak, and contemptuously swept it across Brud's face. Brud staggered backwards into our arms.

Before we had time to recover, the huge figure of John R. came somersaulting over the counter, sending the three men sprawling over tables and drinks. Picking themselves up, Big-Mouth's brother and his companion quickly decided discretion was the better part of valour. Too well they knew and feared John's reputation. Big-mouth also knew, but drink and pride left him no alternative but a standing defiance. As John approached to throw him out after his companions, he aimed a vicious kick at his lower regions, barely missing the target. A crushing right from John's huge fist sent Big-Mouth sprawling on the floor. Then John grabbed Big-Mouth by the knees and chest, lifted him above his head and with a roar like a bull threw him over the wooden partition, to go crashing through the plate glass window onto the street.

Standing for some seconds shaking with emotion, John slowly walked behind the counter and ordered the barman to set up a drink for everybody in the bar.

"A nice how-do-you-do," said Cathy as we settled down.

"You should have left him to me," Brud told John R. to all-round laughter.

"A nice home-coming sure enough," Cathy went on. "I bet you never saw a carry-on like that in all your travels."

"Indeed no, Cathy," I lied. "Sure you'd get the likes of that nowhere only Listowel."

I caught sight of Roger coming through the front door and without speaking to anybody go through to the back. Emerging soon afterwards with a brush and bucket. Ten minutes later he was back. "I'll nail a few boards on the window when the crowd goes", he told John R. Then putting his hand on the Bruds shoulder he gazed admiringly at the pint and small whiskey placed before him. "A thing of beauty is a joy forever", he declared. " 'pon me soul, I heard the crash of that glass and me lying in me bed."

"I've been waiting a long time to ask you for a favour," he said to the Brud, as he put the now empty glass back on the counter.

"If my guess is right Roger, you're only five or six

years too late. Gone like the snows of last winter."

"Yerra, try one bar," Roger persisted, "just between the four of us."

"You're a terrible hoor, Roger," Brud scolded, "but I swear you're asking the impossible."

Roger put on a look of great hurt and disappointment.

"Give him one verse, nice and low," Cathy urged. "Can't you see he's determined to get his way as usual."

Three more small ones and three pints appeared like magic on the counter, along with a small glass of wine for Cathy. The Brud pushed his drinks to the middle of the counter, then, leaning one elbow beside them , he commenced to sing. An instant hush fell on the bar. "There is a cailin fair as May... for a year and for a day......"

The familiar unique voice was free of strain and miraculously loud and clear. Without a shadow of doubt, even the most impressive singers I had heard were not in the same class. The thought flashed across my mind, how lucky it was my mother was not here. Out of the corner of my eye, I could see a single tear slowly trickle down Cathy's cheek, to be instantly brushed away with the back of her hand. The applause was long and sincere, as Brud took the pint in both hands and winked at Cathy.

I said my goodbyes at their front door, painfully aware that Brud was more than anxious to tumble into bed.

I might have known my father would not miss the chance of an extra hand in the bog.

" 'twill make up for the lost day, besides the fresh air will do you the world of good. You can change in the bog," he said, throwing me an old pair of flannels. "Your uncles Jimmy and Thadeen are coming to give us a hand."

"The crack should be good," I said, "if they don't start fighting."

"I'll tip Thadeen off to ignore him," my father said. "We must avoid an upheaval in the firm at any cost."

From the word go, Jimmy's taunts met with a strict policy of silence. I wondered how long it could last.

"I'd ate a calf," Jimmy said as we sat down for lunch.

"That's the worst of the bog," he went on. "It gives you a fierce appetite and a terrible thirst. A nice pint would go well now. Don't you agree Thadeen?"

"Ah! kiss me arse," Thadeen snapped.

"I hear the Growler is back from London," my father said, anxious to change the subject.

"Another pain in the arse," Thadeen snapped. "One week in London, his only time ever out of the bog, and he has more to say than Marco Polo. All the knives they had on the table for the daughter's wedding. All the courses, and Champagne. *Two priests* if you don't mind."

"Ah you're only jealous," Jimmy cut in. "I hear she married a millionaire. Aren't they gone to

America for their honeymoon?"

"I don't know what they're gone to America for," Thadeen snapped. "If it's the same old hoor she brought home last year, 'twill be some honeymoon."

"Any notion of taking the plunge yourself?" Jimmy asked. He knew this was a sore point.

"One more word and I'll stick this pike up your arse," Thadeen threatened.

"There's something burning!" my father said, jumping up. I looked over his shoulder.

"It's my suit," I cried. I'd folded it so carefully and put it on a clump of heather.

"It's goosed," my father declared, as he grabbed the pike and tossed the smouldering garments into the bog hole.

"Somebody must have flicked a butt or a match," Jimmy said. "Rule me out anyhow, you all know I don't smoke."

"Will you listen to the bastard!" Thadeen shouted.

I'll look well heading for London in these flannels, I thought.

R OGER was entertaining a cattle jobber in Scanlon's. "Leaving already?" he enquired. "It's a terror the way time flies. What a pity you can't stay a bit longer."

"I had a good day in the bog, Roger."

"Ah well," he said, "that's enough for any man. Only for the likes of yourself and the odd decent jobber that comes around I'd be as well going off with you to London."

The jobber smiled. "Three pints, Eddie," he called.

John Guerrin put his head in the door. "Ready any time you are...."

"See you in half an hour," the jobber replied. "In the Arms Hotel."

"I'm going to Limerick with Mr Saunders," John said. "Fancy coming along for the crack?"

"A great idea," I said. I was glad of the company, even though it would mean paying the single bus fare from there to Dublin.

T HE time had passed so quickly. That day in the bog and my lovely new suit, I would think about for a long time. "Just typical," I could hear Ann say. How Thadeen kept his temper with Uncle Jimmy's teasing was a miracle. I smiled at the roguery and technique of the bold Roger. A self-made man! He should have been a politician.

The bus conductor disturbed my thoughts. "Nenagh," he announced.

"All back in ten minutes," he warned as the passengers scrambled towards the pub. Through the window I could see a tall man lift up a little girl and kiss her. Then after a quick kiss for his wife and the small child in her arms, the tall man boarded the bus and sat on the front seat. The little girl climbed onto the bus and kissed him once again.

"Go to your mammy, Kathleen," he said. "I'll send you a nice present from England."

The little girl joined her Mammy and baby

brother in the street. The man looked straight ahead. His wife was a beautiful woman, hardly more than twenty-four.

The driver took his seat.

"All aboard, we're five minutes late already," the conductor shouted. The tall man stood up as the engine started, and pulled down the window with a bang.

"Mary," he said hoarsely. "About that saddle. I've changed my mind." Mary took a half step nearer the window. Her lips moved but no words came. The small girl had her face buried in her mother's coat. Mary stretched out her free hand and placed it gently on the huge hand of her husband. "Mary," he said in a tense voice, "tell Sullivan he can have the saddle for fifty shillings."

God Almighty! Will this bloody bus never move?

Somebody at the back of the bus started up a lively tune on a mouth organ. The tall man slumped back in his seat. I closed my eyes and the conductor rang the bell....

Epilogue

HOW many people perished on the high seas fleeing from terror and famine nobody will ever know. Certain it is, had this voyage lasted much longer, few on board would have survived to tell the tale. Compared with this, my voyage on the 'Kyle Clare' now seemed like a Mediterranean cruise. It was hard to believe that today almost a hundred years after the notorious coffin ships, people could still be treated like animals. Worse. At least the animals were protected from the elements.

The deck was strewn with luggage. There was evidence everywhere of failure to make it to the filthy toilets or the rails. I heard the high-pitched scream of a young baby as the ship took yet another dip with the subsequent monotonous swish of spray and water.

"Never again!" The girl's voice came from behind a heavy scarf wound about her face.

"This your first time?" I got the question in as the ship levelled out before another mountainous wave sent it rocking.

"Hold on to her nibs before we all smother," a second voice said. It came from a huge pile of clothing on my left. A pair of arms held forth a little girl of four or five. I grabbed the child and without any fuss she nestled in my arms.

The face behind the heavy scarf emerged. "Tell us your name," she asked the child. At a glance I was struck with the beauty of the girl.

"Joan," the child replied.

"That's a coincidence," the girl said. "My name is Joan too."

"We're all going to see my Dad," the child confided.

A second child now emerged from the bundle, clearly bent on joining his sister. "I'll take Joan", big Joan said. "You grab Curly before he's blown away."

Wrapping my overcoat around Curly, I could hear the woman in the bundle laughing. From where Curly had emerged, a third small face had appeared. Now all three of us were laughing to the obvious puzzlement of the children.

Once again the baby's shrill cry rang clear above the wind, the waves, the ship's engines and the laughter.

"She misses the heat," the woman said. "Hold on to her while I go to the toilet."

"Mind you don't get blown overboard," I warned.

A huge figure lying a few feet away rose to his feet. "I'll give you a hand across the deck," he said. Instantly I recognised the man whose farewell at Nenagh had given me the shivers. The woman still holding the baby, the man's arms around her shoulders, they went swaying across the deck, leaving Joan and me with the uncomplaining trio.

One of the crew came to look around. "Won't be long now," he shouted.

"Thank God," Joan said. "I was certain our end had come. Those seamen must have nerves of steel to risk their lives over and over again."

"Have you a job to go to?" I asked.

"Oh! yes," she replied. "I'm going to work in a bank." Once again we roared laughing. "It's the truth," she blustered. "My uncle is doing well in London. He managed to get me an interview in Dublin and here I am."

"When I think of the bank clerks at home, I just can't see any of them travelling like this."

"They are a class apart sure enough," she agreed. "I wouldn't have the remotest chance of getting into a bank in Ireland."

I marvelled at the idea of such a young girl taking up a job in a bank anywhere.

THE ships siren told us we were at last approaching the harbour. All over the deck people stirred into life, eager to make a speedy exit. Anxious as they were, all waited patiently as people with children were ushered to the front of the queue. The woman led the way with the baby, followed closely by Joan, the big man and myself bearing our precious loads, to be among the first to enter the train for London.

No sooner had the train begun to move than the sound of the mouth organ came wafting from the next carriage. The young crowd joined in the songs, undaunted by the grim voyage they had endured or by what might lie ahead. Waking after a short nap, I turned to find Joan sleeping soundly. Curly lay contented in her arms, likewise out for the count.

Almost before we knew it the train was pulling into Euston Station.

"Wish we could all meet again," Joan said. "I haven't a clue what branch of the bank I'll be sent to. Here's my uncle's address. If you're ever around Wembley call and see us."

"You'd never know," I said, as the train jerked to a halt.

WHAT a relief to be walking on solid ground. In spite of the nightmare sea trip, the joy of seeing my mother and father had more than compensated for all the hardship. The saddest moment had been parting with Brud - my childhood hero, unequalled on the football field, now grimly battling against a cruel enemy with no hope of escape. I could still hear his haunting rendering of 'The Snowy Breasted Pearl'.

Oxford Street was already shaping up for another great shopping spree. People browsed before the huge shop windows enjoying the warm mid-day sunshine. A group of Americans were intently studying the smart display of fur coats. I felt like drawing their attention to the brickwork. Maybe if I stared through that glass long enough the figure of Eileen would appear.

The taxi man looked me up and down dubiously. My father's flannels and the limp sleeping bag did not impress him.

"It's okay," I assured him, pulling a few notes

from my pocket.

I paid him at the high wrought-iron gates. "Tell you something," he said. "My old man is in there."

The flower woman at the gate was blind. It was sad that she could not enjoy the lovely display of colour surrounding her. I bought a bunch of flowers and carried them to the grave.

HOW patiently she will listen to all the news from home. How will I explain the destruction of yet another suit? I look at all the messages fluttering in the breeze: heartfelt words of love from friends and fellow workers; nurses, doctors, sisters. On a torn envelope I write my own special message and tuck it into the small bunch of flowers. How peaceful the surroundings are in contrast to the storm inside my head.

My eyes are wet with the tears I am at last able to shed. Not even the warm mid-day sun can do anything to ease the pain, or the chill. Then, as if in a dream, I hear a lark overhead. Looking up I see her clearly - up there on her invisible perch; up there above the lonely mountain in Rathea; up there above the lapping waters of Bundoran; singing for evermore a Requiem for Love.

How long I gazed into the flowers and the memories, I do not know. Wearily I turn away. Through misty eyes I see, slowly approaching along the pathway and carrying a bunch of flowers, the unmistakable form of Ann......